Frontispiece. Early *Kewpie* dolls and figurines created by Rose O'Neill and sculpted by Joseph L. Kallus. At the top is the all-bisque *Kewpie Mountain*, one of the two known examples in existence, in which several *Action Kewpies* reside. From Ralph Griffith's 1984 Rose O'Neill Calendar. *Ralph Griffith Collection.*

Kewpies®

Dolls & Art
with Value Guide - 2nd Edition

by John Axe

Prices provided by Connie Harrell of
The Doll Cradle

Published by Hobby House Press, Inc.
Grantsville, MD 21536
www.hobbyhouse.com

Acknowledgments

The compilation of any book pertaining to collectibles requires the cooperation of a great many people. An author has to rely on the generosity of good friends who share information, pictures and valuable items that they have collected over the years.

I will always be grateful to these generous Kewpie lovers: Bette Ann Axe, Shirley Buchholz, the California Rose O'Neill Association, Ralph Griffith, Wanda Lodwick, Lillian Mosley, Mona Nevins, Grayce Piemontesi, Lillian Rohaly, Patricia N. Schoonmaker, Helen Sieverling and Joyce Stafford.

I am glad that my sister Patricia E. Axe was able to help with the making of index cards and the Index, too.

I am lucky to have the talented staff of Hobby House Press, Inc. bring this project to realization. I am grateful to the Production Department, Editor Donna H. Felger, Managing Editor A. Christian Revi and Publisher Gary R. Ruddell.

Most of all I want to express my appreciation to Nancy Villaseñor President of Jesco, Inc., for her time, her help and generous loan of the Joseph L. Kallus files.

A special thanks to Connie Harrell for providing prices for the value guide.

Additional copies of this book may be purchased at $29.95 (plus postage and handling) from
Hobby House Press, Inc.
I Corporate Drive, Grantsville, MD 21536
1-800-554-1447
www.hobbyhouse.com
or from your favorite bookstore or dealer.

Kewpie and Cameo are trademarks of Jesco, Inc.
All photographs and pictured materials are
Courtesy of Jesco, Inc., except where otherwise noted.

©1987 Hobby House Press, Inc.
1st Reprint - 1990, 2nd Reprint - 2001

Printed in the United States of America

ISBN: 0-87588-589-6

Table of Contents

Kewpie in vinyl with a vinyl *Felix the Cat* from the late 1950s.

PART I

The History of Rose O'Neill
and Joseph L. Kallus

ROSE O'NEILL
The Creator of Kewpie

Illustration 1. Rose O'Neill modeling Scootles, 1920s.

True Art, whether it is found in literature or in the plastic creative mediums, must have excellence of form or expression and it must express ideas of permanent or universal interest. Rose O'Neill's Kewpie has met this criteria for almost 80 years now. Kewpie, an enchanting and charming little elfin creature, was inspired by Rose O'Neill's baby brother and she stated that her Kewpie was the baby form of Cupid, a pagan god of love, "but there is a difference. Cupid gets himself into trouble. The Kewpies get themselves out, always searching out ways to make the world better and funnier."

The Columbian Exposition of 1893 in Chicago celebrated the 400th anniversary of the discovery of America by Columbus. Architects designed a park full of buildings to house the exhibits and displays and these buildings had impressive classic facades and porticoes that revived an interest in that style of architecture. Classical motifs in art and decoration became popular once more and Ancient Greece was the inspiration for another romantic movement.

This was the last part of the Victorian era and there was more freedom of creativity for both men and women and new expressions in art and in literature were sought and expressed. The leading centers of intellectual activity were the rapidly growing cities in both Europe and America.

The cosmopolitan life attracted artists and intellectuals and many of them went to Europe to study and to live in sophisticated settings like romantic Paris. Several talented American women were drawn to the romantic movement. Gertrude Stein (1874-1946) lived in Paris after 1903 and her home became a center for artists and writers, such as Henri Matisse, Pablo Picasso, Sherwood Anderson, Ezra Pound, Ernest Hemingway and John

Illustration 2. Rose O'Neill's first published drawing, *Temptation*, which appeared in the Omaha *World Herald* in 1889 when she was 14. Note that she signed her name at the foot of the fleeing figure.

Reed. Isadora Duncan (1878-1927), who revolutionized the dance by drawing her inspiration from nature, the "god" of the romantics, lived in Europe after 1902. She danced barefoot in a loose tunic, suggested by Greek sculpture, and furthered the 20th century emancipation in women's dress with her unique costumes.

Rose O'Neill's life and work were formed in this same intellectual atmosphere and time. The classical past and the romantic movement had a great impact on her creative forces.

Rose O'Neill was an illustrator, a sculptor, a designer, an artist, a novelist, a poet and she was a totally original individualist. She was a true "Renaissance Woman" who utilized and explored her many talents and interests and left behind a great creative legacy that is still studied and admired. Of all her many works and projects, the one that will always be the best known is her Kewpie. Even people who have never heard of Rose O'Neill have heard of *Kewpie* dolls; even people who could not accurately describe a *Kewpie* doll know that it is something cute and clever. The little nude, chubby Kewpies with their wry topknots of hair first began as magazine illustrations but their most popular form has always been dolls and figurines. Everyone loves to look at Kewpies; no one can resist touching and holding a Kewpie that is in a modeled form. Kewpies amuse and delight and they make one smile and most of all they are the artistic expression of a woman who knew how to enjoy life.

Cecilia Rose O'Neill was born on June 25, 1874, in Wilkesbarre, Pennsylvania, the second child of Alice Asenath Cecilia Smith and William Patrick O'Neill, both of whom were talented, creative and artistic. Mr. O'Neill moved his family to Battle Creek, Nebraska, when Rose was three. From an early age Rose's romantic parents instilled in the child their love of the classic authors and the myths of the Greek and Roman gods. The O'Neill parents encouraged Rose to develop her own creative talents, which included drawing, music and writing.

By the time that Rose was 14 the family had moved to Omaha, Nebraska, and she now had six brothers and sisters. In 1889 Rose entered a drawing contest for children sponsored by the Omaha *World Herald*. Her work, called *Temptation* showed a rather immodestly clad, for the times, figure of a woman inspired by classical mythology fleeing along a rocky path. The drawing was so good that the newspaper at first could not believe that it was from the hand of a young girl.

Patrick O'Neill inspired his daughter to join a company of touring actors in 1890 to encourage another aspect of her many talents. Rose was not able to properly interpret the Shakespearean roles that her father loved so much as successfully as they both had hoped so she left the band of strolling players and turned to writing as an outlet for her creative drives. (Reportedly, Rose's father had presented her to Mme. Modjeska, the famous 19th century Shakespearean actress, when Rose was about 14 or 15, and Modjeska had informed her that she was too "sensitive" to compete in Modjeska's profession.)

In 1893 Rose left Omaha for New York City, where she intended to publish a novel she had been working on and to pursue her ambition of drawing illustrations for magazines. Up to that point she was largely self-taught so she enrolled in art classes and had some success illustrating stories for such magazines as *Truth, Harper's Weekly* and *The Great Divide*. Illustrations for magazines was a field dominated by men at that time so Rose signed her works with her initials "C.R.O." to disguise the fact that she was a woman. The year that Rose left for New York her father moved his family to a rural setting in the southern Ozark mountains in Missouri. The O'Neills called their new home Bonniebrook. Bonniebrook, which was basically a rustic cabin at that time, was to have a great influence on Rose O'Neill and it affected the rest of her life. The pastoral serenity of Bonniebrook appealed to Rose's romantic nature and the tranquility of living in a remote district allowed her more time to formulate her future creative visions.

Gray Latham, a young man whom Rose had met while the family was located in Omaha, called on her at Bonniebrook and he and Rose were married in 1896. Rose returned to New York with Latham and worked as an illustrator for *Puck* magazine, signing her drawings "O'Neill-Latham." Latham appeared as the male model in many of Rose's works at this time. Rose's marriage was not a happy one. When not enough money came in the door of their home, love flew out of the window. In 1901 Rose and Latham were divorced and she returned again to Bonniebrook, continuing her career as a magazine illustrator.

About a year after Rose returned to Bonniebrook she married Harry Leon Wilson, *Puck's* literary editor, whom she was not supposed to have met while living in New York, according to several O'Neill biographers. Both Rose and Mr. Wilson resigned their respective positions with *Puck* and moved to Connecticut where they worked at writing novels. In 1904 Rose's first book, *The Loves of Edwy*, was published. Wilson published the classic novels *The Ruggles of Red Gap* and *Merton of the Movies*, among others. By 1930 Rose O'Neill had published three more adult novels — *The Lady in the White Veil* (1909), *Garda* (1929), and *The Goblin Woman* (1930); and a book of poetry, *The Master Mistress* (1922). During this period she also authored four children's books — *The Kewpies and Dottie Darling* (1910), *The Kewpies, Their Book* (1912), *The Kewpie Primer* (1912), and *The Kewpies and the Runaway Baby* (1928). The Wilsons were close friends of Pulitizer-Prize winning novelist Booth Tarkington and his poetess wife and she also did illustrations for their literary works. In 1905 the Wilsons and the Tarkingtons spent the summer in Italy at a villa on the Isle of Capri, where Mr. Wilson and Mr. Tarkington co-wrote the successful Broadway play *The Man From Home*.

After five years as the wife of Harry Leon Wilson, Rose, who was outgoing and vivacious, became disillusioned with Wilson's moods of despair and silence and she divorced him. They reportedly remained supportive friends afterwards.

Rose O'Neill returned to Bonniebrook in the Ozarks again. Supposedly she was melancholy because of the disappointments in her life and she became more introspective and reflective. At Bonniebrook she claimed that little elfin creatures appeared to her in a dream. She reported in the *Woman's Home Companion* in 1910 that "they were all over my room, on my bed, and one perched on my hand. I awoke seeing them everywhere. Because they felt cold, I knew that they were elves." Rose drew pictures of these little creatures who had plump nude bodies and a small topknot of hair. For several years she had drawn similar chubby little babies for her illustration work. The elf-like creatures who visited Rose O'Neill in her dreams first appeared as magazine illustrations for the *Woman's Home Companion* in December of 1909. These charming little imps became popular immediately and Rose was commissioned to create them for various publications and for advertisements. This was the beginning of Kewpie.

Kewpie soon became big business for Rose O'Neill and the demand for various forms of Kewpie was overwhelming. Soon he was to appear in every possible medium, from drawings and illustrations to dolls and figurines in various forms and materials. In 1913 Rose O'Neill obtained a copyright for this very original and unique little character. Three-quarters of a century later the craze still exists for Rose O'Neill's Kewpie in all forms.

Rose needed assistance in managing and marketing the Kewpie properties. By 1912 Geo. Borgfeldt & Co. of New York had become interested in developing a line of *Kewpie* figurines and dolls. For this project the Borgfeldt

Illustration 3. Rose O'Neill's Kewpie.

Illustration 4. Original Rose O'Neill artwork for the book *The Kewpies and the Runaway Baby*, 1928.

company and Rose required the assistance of additional artists and sculptors. An advertisement was sent to the Fine Arts College of Pratt Institute in Brooklyn. Interested young artists who could draw and sculpt children were asked to present themselves to Fred Kolb of Borgfeldt, a distributor of dolls, toys and novelty items, and apply for the position of developing a line of *Kewpie* novelties. Seventeen-year-old Joseph Kallus of Brooklyn, who was studying at Pratt Institute on a scholarship, was selected for the *Kewpie* project after Rose O'Neill had approved his work. It was decided that the dolls and figurines would be produced in Germany, where Borgfeldt had connections and where porcelain production was more economical than in the United States.

Callista, Rose O'Neill's younger sister, was studying art in Italy at this time. Rose traveled to Europe to encourage Callista to be her business manager and to help oversee production of *Kewpies* abroad. While she was in Italy Rose traveled to Capri to visit Charles Caryl Coleman, a friend of her father, who owned the Villa Narcissus there. Coleman was an elderly and wealthy artist who was captivated by the young and beautiful Rose O'Neill and reportedly wanted to make her the inheritor of his properties in Italy. To avoid entangling Italian inheritance laws Rose purchased the Villa Narcissus from Coleman for a modest sum. Coleman and his staff continued to live in the villa until his death in 1929 at age 96. He left Rose his collection of paintings and art treasures that he had collected during his long life.

Rose and Callista returned to the United States in about 1918 because of the dangers of the World War and shared an apartment at 61 Washington Square in New York. In the meantime Rose continued her Kewpie drawings that illustrated her poems for *Woman's Home Companion* and *Good Housekeeping*. These projects and the royalties from *Kewpie* figurines and dolls made Rose O'Neill wealthy. Her income permitted her to remodel Bonniebrook in Missouri into a comfortable 14 room house.

At this time Rose began to express a unique personal taste in her manner of dress. She now preferred to wear flowing gowns made of filmy materials, such as she had seen in artwork from the period of Classical Greece while in Europe. At her apartment on Washington Square, New York, she entertained other artists, writers and intellectuals whose company she enjoyed. During this period the popular song "Rose of Washington Square" was written by Ballard McDonald with music by James F. Hanlery and copyrighted by Shapiro, Bernstein & Co. in 1919. Rose O'Neill experts feel that the creator of Kewpie was the inspiration for this popular tune, which has mostly been associated with comedienne Fanny Brice. ("Rose of Washington Square" was the theme song of the 1939 film of the same title which was a thinly-disguised version of the life story of Miss Brice.)

In 1919 Rose became good friends with a Norwegian couple, Matta and Berger Lie, who were visiting the United States on a business trip. Rose showed the Lie couple her newest drawings which she called her "Sweet Monsters." The Monster drawings are a series of voluptuous and sensuous nude figures, including fauns, satyrs, centaurs and other mythical creatures, executed in pen and ink. Some of these drawings were translated into sculptures later, such as "The Embrace of the Tree" which

Illustration 5. A satirical Rose O'Neill drawing depicting the Kewpies catching a culprit selling "Counterfeit Kewpies."

Illustration 6. One of Rose O'Neill's "Sweet Monster" drawings, *The Spectator*, from the *Century* magazine, February 1922. Note the similarity to Auguste Rodin's sculpture, *The Thinker*.

Illustration 7. *The Faun Instructs the Poet Upon the Pipes*, a rather erotic "Sweet Monster" drawing by Rose O'Neill, 1920s. These works were considered by O'Neill her "serious work," as opposed to illustrative work, such as Kewpie.

was installed at Bonniebrook during Rose's life. Matta and Berger Lie encouraged Rose to do more work on these themes and invited her to stay with them in Norway where she would be provided with a studio to produce these pagan-like renderings. Rose and Callista traveled to Norway and remained with the Lies for about six months.

While she was in Europe, Rose enrolled in a course at the Paris studios of recently-deceased French artist Auguste Rodin (1840-1917), considered the most important sculptor of his time. Rose's Monster drawings show a great deal of kinship to such Rodin works as *The Thinker* and *Adam and Eve*. Her Monster drawings were exhibited at a gallery in Paris and later at the Wildenstein Gallery in New York.

During her time in Paris Rose also began instruction in the French language with Jeanne Galeron who, in turn, handed her student over to her young brother, Jean. Jean Galeron returned to America with Rose and lived at Bonniebrook for a time until he settled in New York City with Callista's help. (There were rumors that Rose O'Neill had married the much younger French artist but she never confirmed nor denied these reports. Jean Galeron later married an English girl in Los Angeles.)

During the 1920s Rose O'Neill lived well from the profits of her work. She was the highest paid woman illustrator of all time; she was a world traveler; she had well-known friends in the art world in several countries; and she was active in the movement for Women's Suffrage, producing posters and drawings for the cause. During this period she bought a country home in Connecticut which she called Carabas Castle.

It was at Carabas Castle that Rose O'Neill sculpted her newest creation, *Scootles*, the little traveler who "scooted" all over the world. *Scootles* has been more popular in doll form than any other medium, unlike Kewpie who was produced in all media and materials.

In 1937 Rose O'Neill, now 63 years old, sold Carabas Castle and her Washington Square town house and returned home to Bonniebrook in Missouri. She continued to work on new artistic projects and to promote Kewpie. She had negotiated with movie studios in Hollywood to have a movie made featuring Kewpie but this project never reached fruition. A new creation at Bonniebrook was *Ho-Ho*, the little laughing Buddha doll that caused an outcry from Buddhists when it was mass-produced later.

Rose O'Neill died in Springfield, Missouri, at the home of a nephew on April 6, 1944, after having suffered several strokes. She was buried at her beloved Bonniebrook in the family plot alongside her mother and her brother, James. Callista died in 1946. Bonniebrook burned to the ground in 1947.

Before her death, Rose O'Neill had given some of her artwork to the museum of The School of the Ozarks (a college) which is located at Point Lookout, Missouri. Other Rose O'Neill memorabilia pertaining to her life, particularly that associated with her years at Bonniebrook, was preserved by Dr. Bruce Trimble and his wife, Mary. In 1946 the Trimbles purchased a farm near Branson,

Illustrations 7A and 7B. 15½ inch (39cm) *Rose O'Neill*, the 1982 UFDC convention souvenir doll. Porcelain shoulder plate head, lower arms and lower legs; stuffed cloth body. The French human hair wig is brown; the painted eyes are brown. Incised in script on the back of the shoulder plate: "ROSE // KANSAS CITY 1982 LW // MURIEL // KRAMER." The doll was designed by Lita Wilson and executed by Muriel Kramer. The costume is a simple rose colored shift of the sort that Rose O'Neill, herself, typically wore. The doll was presented complete and with a stand as she appears here.

Missouri, which is not far from Bonniebrook. This farm had been the setting of Harold Bell Wright's popular and sentimental novel *The Shepherd of the Hills*. The Trimbles established a museum at the Shepherd of the Hills Farm and in the Rose O'Neill room they exhibited all the artifacts pertaining to her work that they had managed to collect. The Museum of the School of the Ozarks also houses an extensive collection of Rose O'Neill memorabilia, such as *Kewpie* dolls, Rose O'Neill's original artwork and copies of her books.

Collectors have done even more to preserve the memory and the work of Rose O'Neill. Even though the figurines and dolls of Kewpie were first produced as inexpensive novelty items, a vast number of them have been kept in excellent condition and are still seen for sale at doll shows, flea markets and in antique shops. Many collectors have huge collections centered around the designs of Rose O'Neill. Rose O'Neill collectors were first organized in 1967 by Pearl Hodges of Branson, Missouri, who promoted Rose O'Neill week to honor the creator of Kewpie. This event led to the formation of the National and International Rose O'Neill Clubs, with several affiliates, the largest being the California Rose O'Neill Association.

Each year Branson, Missouri, hosts the annual Rose O'Neill Kewpiesta to promote and preserve the memory of Rose O'Neill and her Kewpies. The International Rose O'Neill Club has sponsored such efforts as archeological digs at the site of Bonniebrook to search for *Kewpie* parts

and other items that may have survived the fire of 1947. In 1974 the admirers of Rose O'Neill encouraged the Governor of Missouri, Christopher S. Bond, to proclaim June 25, 1974, as Rose O'Neill Day in honor of the great Missourian's 100th birthday. Jean Cantwell reported on this event in the *Antique Trader Weekly* of August 27, 1974, and succinctly described the day:

"One hundred years after her birth, the charm, beauty, and ethereal love of Rose O'Neill still permeates the land where she perceived the Kewpies and captured them, with love, on her easel."

The National Rose O'Neill Club of Branson, Missouri, also publishes a biannual "Kewpiesta Kourier" which is sent to its members "to preserve and cherish the memory of Rose O'Neill and to inform the public about her and her works."

The true genius of Rose O'Neill was best exemplified by her ability to seek out or to attract others who inspired her and encouraged her to pursue her artistic and creative endeavors. It is also seen in the love that many thousands of persons have had over the years for her work and for herself as a truly unique woman. If Rose O'Neill had never done anything else except to draw Kewpies, she would still be acknowledged as an important creative talent whose works and designs would always be a part of America's artistic heritage.

Rose O'Neill's philosophy was, "Do good deeds in a funny way. The world needs to laugh, or at least to smile more than it does."

The following Kewpie magazine pages are from *Woman's Home Companion* and *The Ladies' Home Journal,* 1911 through 1927. These whimsical drawings and verses tell the Kewpie story and show some of the paper dolls that were available in the magazines during the height of the "Kewpie Kraze." *Grayce Piemontesi Collection.*

This page is for Children

Kewpie Kutouts
in Many Colors

Every month in Woman's Home Companion

THE Kewpies were invented by Rose O'Neill. They are always doing good, helping Dotty Darling and her Baby Brother to have a good time whenever the older children wouldn't let them tag along. Now all the children want to cut out the Kewpies. And the Kewpies want to be cut out by the children. So Rose O'Neill has made the Kewpie Kutouts. There is a whole page of them for you in the October copy of the Woman's Home Companion—a magazine with pages and pages for children and their mothers.

Wag, the Chief— his back

Wag, the Chief

This is Wag, the Chief. He is captain of the band of Kewpies that have been making things so pleasant for Very Little Folks, whose mothers take the Woman's Home Companion. When you cut him out and paste him together, he makes a real Kewpie whichever way you look at him.

Dotty Darling is over five inches high in the Kewpie Kutout.

Dotty's Baby Brother is not quite so tall as Dotty, because he is younger.

The Kewpies are the first cutouts to have real backs.

In October Woman's Home Companion you will find Wag in color (not plain black and white like he is here) and Dotty Darling (with two dresses) and Dotty's Baby Brother all ready to be cut out.

A delicious story about Dotty Darling and her Kewpies has a page all to itself opposite the Kewpie Kutouts.

Ask your Mother for 15 cents

—then hurry to a news-stand and buy the October Woman's Home Companion, which has the first of the Kewpie Kutouts, or send the 15 cents to us right away with your name and address on the Kewpie Kupon. We will send you by return mail the October Woman's Home Companion, postage paid.

"Use this Kupon"

WOMAN'S HOME COMPANION

at 381 Fourth Avenue, New York

Woman's Home Companion
381 Fourth Ave., New York

Here is my 15c. Please send me right away the October Woman's Home Companion containing the first of the Kewpie Kutouts.

Name _____

Address _____

The Kewpies and Their New Adventures

The Kewps and Dot
again we view
Engaging in adventures
new!

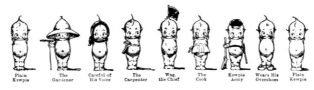

Plain Kewpie · The Gardener · Careful of His Voice · The Carpenter · Wag, the Chief · The Cook · Kewpie Army · Wears His Overshoes · Plain Kewpie

Verse and Pictures
By
Rose O'Neill

1.

IN THIS first picture here we view
The Kewpies dropping from the blue.
The chief says, "Kewps, I'd like to find you
Someone that you could be kind to.

"Now here's a town we might look through
For some good deed that we could do.
Let's find one—concentrate intensely,
Good deeds improve a Kewp immensely."

2.

Well, hardly had they looked
at all,
When in an alley, poor and
small,
They found a poor child
dressed so badly,
Sitting on a door-step sadly.

Before she guessed, before
she knew,
What those brisk Kewps
were going to do,
They had her up above the
crowds there,
Sailing with the birds and
clouds there.

4.

5.

And flying lightly brought her where
Were grassy meadows, green and fair.

They fed her berries for a while, dears,
And then they taught her how to smile, dears.

Next, to improve the shining hours,
They make her pale cheeks pink with flowers.

One Kewpie, in a way that pleases,
Curls her tresses with the breezes.

15

Then suddenly they take her to
A garden bright, with flowers new,
Where gardening becomes a pleasure.
They while the time with work and leisure.

As watering makes flowers grow,
The child treats all their winglets so,
The Kewps submit, and thank her so much,
Though Kewpish wings can never grow much.

And so they passed the afternoon,
And all went merry as a tune.
At last she asked, "Whose garden is it
Where we have this pleasant visit?"

The Kewpies laughed till they were hoarse,
"It's Dotty Darling's home, of course.
And there she comes, and maybe, too,
Behind her comes her baby, too."

Then, oh, the fun these little girls
Had with Kewpish games and whirls!
The poor child laughed as merrily
As any robin in a tree.

And when 'twas time for her to go,
Dot and the baby hugged her so.
And then the Kewps took her away, dears,
But brought her back another day, dears.

At the left is Nancy Villaseñor, the President of Jesco, Inc.; at the right are Mr. and Mrs. James Skahill. Mr. Skahill is Vice President of Jesco, Inc.

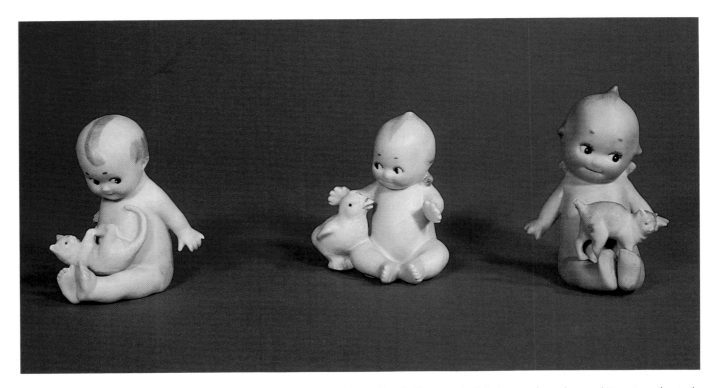

Action Kewpies with cats and a peep. Each is about 3 inches (8cm) tall. Note that the figure at the left does not have the usual *Kewpie* topknot of hair; this is a much rarer version. *Lillian Rohaly Collection.*

Rare *Action Kewpies* that are about 2 inches (5cm) tall. *Lillian Rohaly Collection.*

An unusual and rare *Action Kewpie* that is only 3 inches (8cm) tall. *Lillian Rohaly Collection.*

3½ inch (9cm) *Kewpie Travelers. Lillian Rohaly Collection.* Any figure that includes the Kewpie Doodle Dog is quite rare.

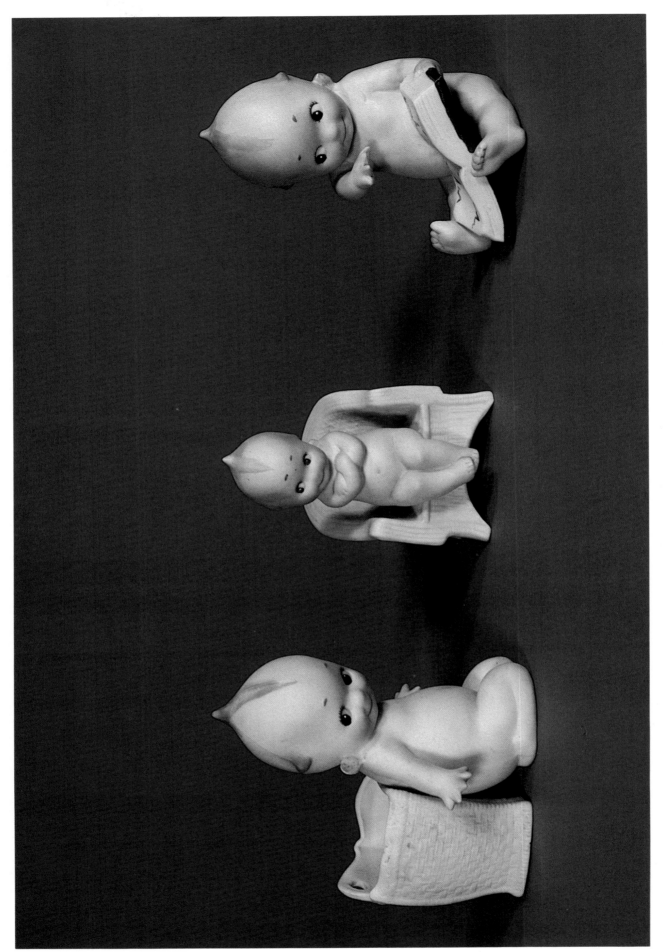

Kewpie action figures that include "The Mayor" in his wicker chair. Each is about 3½ inches (9cm) tall. Lillian Rohaly Collection.

Action Kewpies in unusual forms. The lying soldier at the left is only 2¾ inches (7cm) long. *Lillian Rohaly Collection.*

Kewpie figurines made in Japan by Lefton, 1973. These charmers average about 4 inches (10cm) tall. They are stamped in black: "KW913."

Child's china tea set of Kewpie design. The pieces are all marked: "COPYRIGHT // ROSE O'NEILL WILSON // KEWPIE // GERMANY." *Helen Sieverling Collection.*

4 inch (7cm) tall Indian *Kewpie*, marked "ROSE O'NEILL;" maker unknown, circa 1970s. *Wanda Lodwick Collection.*

DOTTY DARLING AND THE KEWPIES

THE PLEASANT TALE OF HOW AND WHY THE KEWPIES TAUGHT OUR DOT TO FLY

VERSE AND PICTURES BY ROSE O'NEILL

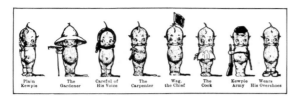

Plain Kewpie   The Gardener   Careful of His Voice   The Carpenter   Wag, the Chief   The Cook   Kewpie Army   Wears His Overshoes

"The little wings are put in place,
And oh, the smile on Dotty's face"

'TWAS March, and yet 'twas more like May,
The sun kept shining all the day,
The flowers began to think of springing,
The birds considered nests and singing.
Young Dotty Darling thought of various
Ways of being quite hilarious.
Her little feet kept up a tripping,
Systematic sort of skipping,
All about the hillside snooping,
To see if there were flowers, stooping,
And occasionally whooping.
(Her whooping has no harshness to it,
As Indians and engines do it.
I pause to mention this, at present,
Lest you should think the dear unpleasant.)

"Oh, my!" for joy the maiden sings,
'I _wish_ I had some Kewpie wings!"
No sooner had she said the word.
Than forty little wings were heard.
She looked around—she looked on high,
The Kewps were dropping from the sky.
(Just like a little flock of birds!)

Said Wag, the chief, "What Kewp will lend
His wings here to oblige a friend?"
"Take mine," a dozen Kewpies cried.
"One pair's enough," the Chief replied.
"It's time," he added, "you and I
Should teach our little Dot to fly.
We should have thought of this before
And calculated on it more.

I don't know how it slipped my mind;
Why, something must have tripped my mind!"

With all the Kewpies' easy grace,
The little wings are put in place,
And oh, the smile on Dotty's face!
(I simply can't describe it!)
The little Cook then gaily tries
To start young Dotty toward the skies;

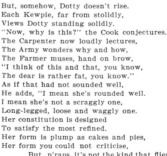

"Oh dear, oh dear what fun she found then,
Flying gaily 'round and 'round then"

But, somehow, Dotty doesn't rise.
Each Kewpie, far from stolidly,
Views Dotty standing solidly.
"Now, why is this?" the Cook conjectures.
The Carpenter now loudly lectures,
The Army wonders why and how,
The Farmer muses, hand on brow,
"I think of this and that, you know,
The dear is rather fat, you know."
As if that had not sounded well,
He adds, "I mean she's rounded well.
I mean she's not a scraggly one,
Long-legged, loose and waggly one.
Her constitution is designed
To satisfy the most refined.
Her form is plump as cakes and pies,
Her form you could not criticise,
But, p'raps, it's not the kind that flies."
The Chief cried, "Nonsense, you stir now,
All together! Boost her now!"

They boosted hard, they boosted high,
To get the darling in the sky.
They pushed so hard, they pushed so fast,
You thought they'd get her up at last.
(But nothing happened.)

Look here," said Wag, "she's only flopping.

We thought it easy, without dropping—
As natural as hop-toads hopping,
But now, in spite of self-reliance,
It's plain that flying is a science.
Now, without further boosts or words,
Let's do like all the mother-birds:
When teaching baby birds to go,
They just keep flying to and fro,
Depending mainly on example,
So now let's give this child a sample."
(And that's exactly what they did.)

Well, Dotty watched those Kewpies skitting
'Round about with easy flitting,
And at the end of twenty minutes
Her wings were waving like a linnet's.
Up she went among the lot there,
And hardly knew just how she got there.
She said, "I never thought I'd be
An aëronaut like this, you see."
Oh dear, oh dear, what fun she found then,
Flying gaily 'round and 'round then,
The only child in all the world,
That ever flew and wheeled and whirled.
The only one that we've had word of—
At least, the only one _I've_ heard of.

"They boosted hard, they boosted high,
To get the darling in the sky"

"Well, Dotty watched those Kewpies skitting
'Round about with easy flitting"

The Kewpies' Christmas Party

Verse and Pictures by Rose O'Neill

This tells of how a palace splendid
Was used for something not intended—
And how some children were befriended.

Wag,
the Chief

And if some wealthy persons knew, dears,
They'd wish that they had been there too, dears,
At least, if they're like me and you, dears.

I.   In this first picture here, we've caught
The little Kewpies plunged in thought.
The way to spend their Christmas best now
Occupies each Kewpie breast now.

IV. With pleasant smiles and movements light,
They gather children left and right;
They dry the tears of little snufflers,
And wrap them well in capes and mufflers.

II. At last, said Wag, "Let's go to where
Rich persons dwell in palace fair;
Abroad they'll spend their Christmas leisure,
I think they'll lend their house with pleasure."

The
Gardener

V.   They gather children all the day,
Children sad and children gay,
Pale, ragged little girls and others,
Sad youngsters minding baby brothers.

Wears His
Overshoes

III. The wealthy persons feel surprise,
But yield to Kewpies firm and wise;
Then out the band flies, brisk and hearty,
To find poor children for their party.

Careful
of His Voice

VI. And as to babies—oh, the fun!
They bundled up each little one,
They took them from their play or slumbers,
In most extraordinary numbers.

The Kindly Kewpies: Verses and Pictures by Rose O'Neill

*This tells of how the
Kewpie lot
Found three bad children—
and, with Dot,
Reformed them promptly
on the spot.*

*They showed them how
to mend their ways
And win their mother's
gentle praise:
So they were good for
days and days.*

I. Upon a morning bright and fair
Four boys were sailing kites in air:
"Some birds are on our kites," they cried there,
Then jumped about with joy and pride there.

II. The kites were high, and their mistake
Was quite an easy one to make;
But if they *could* have seen o'erhead then,
I wonder *what* they would have said then!

III. For, sailing calmly to and fro,
The Kewps are sitting in a row:
With thoughtful chat they while the time there,
And contemplate some deed sublime there.

IV. Said Wag, at last, "Well, let's hop down,
And see what's going on in town."
The boys who saw them lightly dropping—
Well, their eyes were simply popping!

V. The window that they first looked through
Brings such a painful scene to view—
Three children in the dumps, all scowling,
Pouting, cross as bears, and growling.

VI. With calling names and throwing things
Their time flies by as if on wings;
Their mother, from this scene so trying,
Has hidden in the attic, crying.
The Kewps begin to try with care
To clear the situation there:

VII. They mingle good advice with joking;
They try a little playful poking;
They lecture hard, they lecture more;
They try gymnastics on the floor;
Reproaches, reprimands, and teasing
Vie with acrobatics pleasing.

VIII. Get Dotty Darling;
now, *she* could
Help teach these
children to be good.
Now see her gayly
chaffing there!
That crosspatch baby's
laughing there!

IX. Now Dot and Kewpies
bid good-by:
The mother comes
with tearful eye.
Then, oh, surprise and
joy beguiling!
Her children all so
good and smiling!

How the Kewps Turned into Dolls

Verses and Pictures by Rose O'Neill

'TIS nearly May! oh, dear, oh,
dear!
The darling month of all the
year!
The winter wanes on weary wing,
The world is comforted with spring.
Young flowers console the lonely places
With the sweetness of their faces.
The birds are coming, mile on mile,
Our northern sadness to beguile.
The trees all nurse their buds and smile.
They nurse their buds and cling to them,
And talk of splendid spring to them,
Of lovely leaves they sing to them.
They rock their buds on every breeze,

"Why, certainly," said Wag, and
smiled.
"There's Kewps
enough for every
child.
There's Kewps
enough by tens and
dozens
For all the children
and their cousins.
In Kewpie Land, that
paradise,
They're *always* making fresh supplies."
(Which is quite true, you know.)

"*Quick, run and get the rest of us. Put doll clothes on the best of us*"

He falls off walls, or trees, or mountains, maybe,
Because he's bent on
being like a baby.
At stubbing toes, he is a
wonder too.
(See one tied up.) We
call him Blunderboo.

"And now, dear Dot,
that's all I'll name
to-day;
Let's talk, instead, of
why we came to-day.
As o'er your roof we
Kewps were swishing
now,
We heard our Dot en-
gaged in wishing, now.
And down we dropped.
So, dear, proceed to
mention

"*He gives you information on the spot*"

Oh, what a lark!" the Kewpies cried.
(Great excitement!)

"*Poor* children first," cried Dotty Dar-
ling,
And off each Kewp flew like a starling.
They carried boxes for a week or two,
And sometimes there would be a squeak
or two
(They'd hear it, though the Kewps
were chaffing so)
From inside, where the "doll" was
laughing so.
And children—when those dolls came
to them!
Thrills of rapture went right through
them!
"Oh, look!" they'd cry. "Oh, look at
this one!
Oh, let me, let me, let me kiss one!"
(Those Kewps made the *best*
behaved dolls!)

Those blissful, kissful, mother trees.
They lull their buds with melodies.
And while they're gently holding
them
(No hurrying or scolding them),
They're softly—*soft*—unfolding them.
(Oh, sweet mother trees!)

"And now," said Dotty Darling mild,
"With happiness I'm nearly wild.
I wish that every single child
Could have a Kewpie for its own,
To stay with it and play with it
And just *belong* to it alone.
If it *could* be—for every tree
Has its *own* buds; that's plain to see.
And if the Kewpies really could
Arrange it so, I wish they would,—
Beginning, please, with Babe and me,—
That's if they *might,* conveniently."
(And what do you suppose—?)

No sooner had she finished speaking
Than she heard the door a-creaking,
And there was all the Kewpie band
With thousands more from Kewpie
Land.
"Dear me!" said Dotty, are there *more?*
Such crowds I never saw before!"

"Dear me!" said Dot, "look, here are
two loves
That look to me distinctly new loves!"
"Permit me, I shall introduce a few."
Said Wag, "Of course we'll have to lose
a few.
In such a crowd you can't get *all* the
names;
You simply can't, somehow, recall the
names.
But here's the first, the wisest of the lot,
He gives you information on the spot.
All points he settles with a look, you
know,
At his extraordinary book, you know.
On trips, Instructive Kewps are good,
besides
For finding Lat. and Longitude, besides.
The next new Kewpie offered for in-
spection
With a sunbonnet cares for his com-
plexion.
The next wears life preservers, quick to
clap on,
As one can never tell just *what* may
happen.
This little chap has really great renown:
The only Kewp that's always falling
down.

Your wish, as
sured you
have our
rapt atten-
tion."
(Thus Wag
finished his
rather long
speech.)

"I *did* wish
something,
with a great
big W.
But, really, I
am so afraid
'twould
trouble
you,"
So Dot re-
joined,
grown rath-
er shy, at
once.
But all the
Kewpies
make reply
at once,
And look
particularly
spry, at
once.
So Dot takes courage, and says, mod-
estly,
"I wished that you'd turn into dolls,
you see.
So every single childie could have
one
To stay with it and play with it."
The Kewps replied, "No sooner said
than done.
'Twill be the most resplendent bit of
fun!
Quick, run and get the rest of us.
Put doll clothes on the best of us.
Bring boxes now and get inside.
With ribbons every box be tied!

"*We'll turn back into Kewps again*"

And Dot and Baby Brother, too,
Kissed theirs enough to smother
two,
"If children should be *bad,* of course,
Unkind and cross and mad, of course,"
The Kewpie dolls said, "then, with
pain,
We'll turn back into Kewps again,
And off we'll fly in little flocks
And leave them just an empty box.
But, thanks to goodness, children bad
Are *very* seldom to be had.
At least, 'tis sure there aren't many;
In fact, we don't believe there's *any.*"
(And I *do* hope they were right!)

*They carried boxes for
a week or two*

The Flying Kewpies

A New and Fascinating Kewpish Family

By Rose O'Neill

(To find out all about them, read the verses on page 15)

The Life Preserver Kewpie

The Kewpie Life Preserver

Back of Life Preserver Kewpie

CUT out the life belt you see at the right and paste it neatly and firmly around the middle of this Kewpie. He always wears a life preserver buckled around his waist when flying—as he says, you never can tell *what* may happen

TO MAKE the Flying Kewpies, first cut out both back and front views carefully. Just before you paste the back and front together, place the end of a string between the front and the back of the head. Put a slight weight on the Kewpie to keep him flat, and when he is dry you can hang him up by his string from the chandelier, and play he is flying

NO WONDER this Kewpie wears a life preserver. Frobably he thinks that the little boy or girl who pastes the string into his head won't use enough glue. What would happen then? An awful tumble! He might even have to be tied up like Blunderboo

Careful of his Complexion

Blunderboo, the Kewpie that is always tumbling

Back of Careful of his Complexion

CAREFUL of his Complexion, you see, wears a sunbonnet tied under his chin. This protects his face from the breeze when he is flying fast, and shades his eyes from sunshine and lamplight. Watch how gaily the strings and ruffle flutter when he flies

JUST suppose Careful of his Complexion should get freckles! Or tan his nose! A dreadful thought! So he wears a sunbonnet, which he knows looks very cunning. No doubt he has a jar of cold cream somewhere to use after long flying trips

Instructive Kewpie

Back of Blunderboo

BLUNDERBOO, the Kewpie that is always tumbling, wears one toe tied up because he likes to pretend that he has stubbed it, like a real baby. If Blunderboo had *really* stubbed his toe he would not be looking so cheerful

Back of Instructive Kewpie

CUT out the back and front of Instructive Kewpie's big book at the right and paste them together. Then press Instructive Kewpie's arms forward to clasp it against his breast. His eyes may *just* peep out over the edge of the book. How wise Instructive Kewpie looks! He has studied so much that he knows his book by heart

INSTRUCTIVE Kewpie can fly as far and fast as any of the other Flying Kewpies, in spite of his fat book. The print in the "Compendium of Useful Knowledge" is so fine that Instructive Kewpie has to wear large glasses with horn rims, like a real teacher. You see, he almost ruined his eyesight once, reading while flying

The Kewpie Kutouts

Little Assunta and Her Kewpie Doll

By Rose O'Neill

Children, look on page 15 if you want to read the story of Little Assunta and the Kewpie Doll

This is the back of Kewpie Doll. Cut it out and paste to the cut-out front of Kewpie Doll. Bend up standard, and he is done

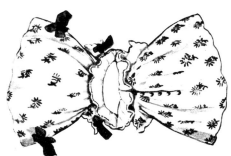

Cut out Kewpie Doll's little flower dress and slit it down the line of buttons in the back

KEWPIE DOLL

NOTICE Kewpie Doll's dress. It is, you see, sprinkled with little red daisies and tied with four red ribbons to match. Kewpie Doll wears a flower dress because it is June and there are flowers growing everywhere, except in city streets. Kewpie Doll knows of yellow buttercups in fields and pink roses in gardens. Perhaps Kewpie Doll thinks that flowers in a dress are better than no flowers at all for Little Assunta, who lives in the slums. When you have slipped the dress over Kewpie Doll's little peaked topknot and wings, be sure to bend back the ribbon bows on the sleeves and on the skirt to hold it neatly

THE red dress is Little Assunta's best one. It is just the color of her father's working shirt and her mother's big silk handkerchief, which she ties over her head when she goes on the street. There are at least five holes in Little Assunta's best dress, and the very biggest one has not been mended yet. Maybe Little Assunta's mother had no more patches, or maybe she is so busy taking care of Little Assunta's brothers and sisters that she doesn't have time to sew. Very likely when Little Assunta sees how clean and neat Kewpie Doll's dress is, she will beg her mother to mend the hole, even if the patch has to be purple, or pink, or green, or yellow

Cut out around the ragged edges of Assunta's red dress, and slit down the line of buttons

THIS is sad Little Assunta before Kewpie Doll found her sitting forlornly beside the garbage barrel. She is very, very poor, and wears a ragged dress and shoes that are out at the toes. She has no nice place to play, like little country children—only dark, dirty streets, instead of picnic woods and hayfields. Little Assunta hasn't even a dolly—or she didn't have till Kewpie Doll came flying along. How her black eyes sparkled when she saw Kewpie Doll and hugged him tight!

LITTLE ASSUNTA

THIS is the back view of Little Assunta. Cut it out carefully and paste to the front view. Then lay Little Assunta under a light weight so that she will be smooth and flat. Bend up the red name plate, and let her stand by herself.

Little Assunta has on her every-day dress which, you see, she once tore terribly on a nail sticking out from an old egg crate. Her red dress, too, has had hard wear. When you cut it out be careful not to jab any more holes in it with your scissors. Slip it gently over Little Assunta's head and bend the ribbons back to hold it on. You cannot possibly be as poor and sad as Little Assunta, but maybe the Kewpie doll will make you happy sometimes

Dotty and Four of Her Kewpie Friends
By Rose O'Neill

Kewpie Gardener

Cut out the front and back view of each Kewpie and paste the front view carefully to the back view. Lay the Kewpie under a weight while the paste is drying. Bend the red pedestal forward so that the Kewpie can stand by himself. Be sure to paste Wag's flag and Kewpie Gardener's rake right where they belong

Back of Careful of His Voice

Wag, the Kewpie Chief

Careful of his Voice

This back view of the Kewpie Gardener is to be cut out and pasted carefully to the front view

Cut out the Kewpie Cook's apron and bend the strings back so that he can wear it as he does in the pictures on the preceding page

Cut out this back view of Dotty Darling and paste on the back of the front view. Then cut out carefully Dotty Darling's everyday dress, and cut it down the back as far as the buttons go, so that you can slip the dress over Dotty's head and let it rest on her shoulders. After this, secure by folding back the tabs

Kewpie Cook

Dotty Darling stands alone if you bend the red pedestal forward

DOTTY DARLING and her br... friends were so popu... ...ey first appeared th...

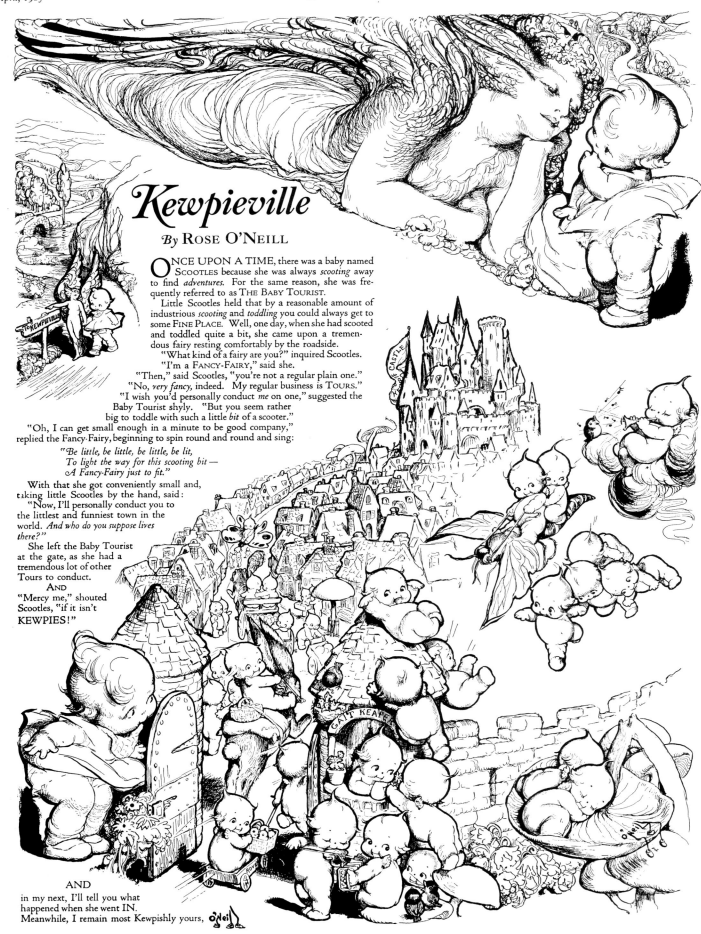

Kewpieville

By ROSE O'NEILL

ONCE UPON A TIME, there was a baby named SCOOTLES because she was always *scooting* away to find *adventures*. For the same reason, she was frequently referred to as THE BABY TOURIST.

Little Scootles held that by a reasonable amount of industrious *scooting* and *toddling* you could always get to some FINE PLACE. Well, one day, when she had scooted and toddled quite a bit, she came upon a tremendous fairy resting comfortably by the roadside.

"What kind of a fairy are you?" inquired Scootles.

"I'm a FANCY-FAIRY," said she.

"Then," said Scootles, "you're not a regular plain one."

"No, *very fancy,* indeed. My regular business is TOURS."

"I wish you'd personally conduct *me* on one," suggested the Baby Tourist shyly. "But you seem rather big to toddle with such a little *bit* of a scooter."

"Oh, I can get small enough in a minute to be good company," replied the Fancy-Fairy, beginning to spin round and round and sing:

> *"Be little, be little, be little, be lit,*
> *To light the way for this scooting bit —*
> *A Fancy-Fairy just to fit."*

With that she got conveniently small and, taking little Scootles by the hand, said:

"Now, I'll personally conduct you to the littlest and funniest town in the world. *And who do you suppose lives there?"*

She left the Baby Tourist at the gate, as she had a tremendous lot of other Tours to conduct.

AND

"Mercy me," shouted Scootles, "if it isn't KEWPIES!"

AND

in my next, I'll tell you what happened when she went IN.

Meanwhile, I remain most Kewpishly yours,

Kewpieville

By
ROSE O'NEILL

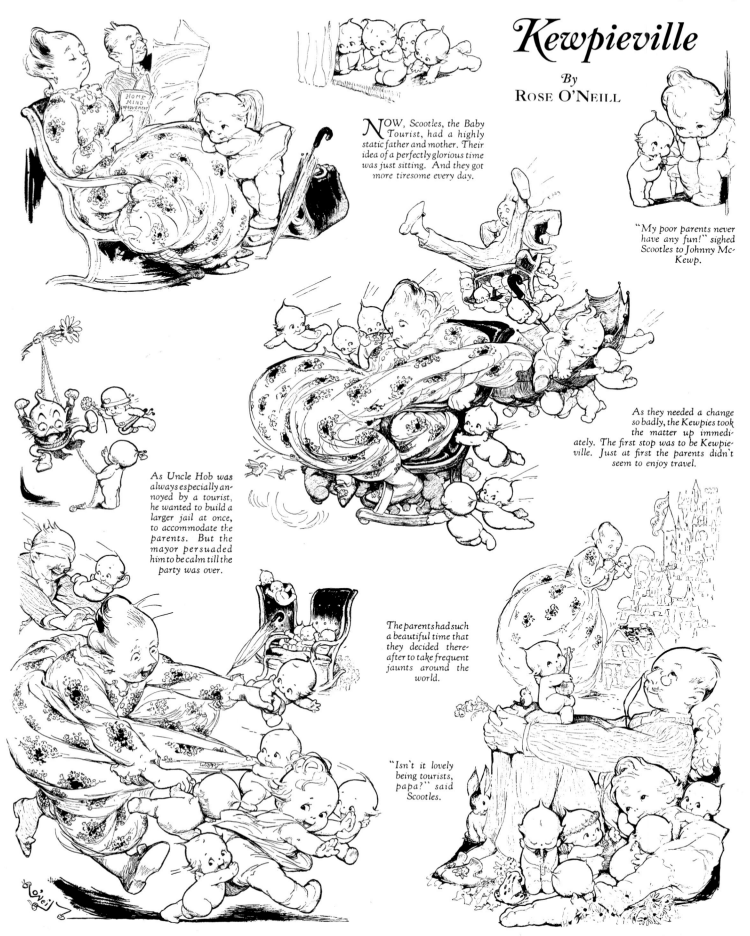

NOW, Scootles, the Baby Tourist, had a highly static father and mother. Their idea of a perfectly glorious time was just sitting. And they got more tiresome every day.

"My poor parents never have any fun!" sighed Scootles to Johnny Mc-Kewp.

As they needed a change so badly, the Kewpies took the matter up immediately. The first stop was to be Kewpieville. Just at first the parents didn't seem to enjoy travel.

As Uncle Hob was always especially annoyed by a tourist, he wanted to build a larger jail at once, to accommodate the parents. But the mayor persuaded him to be calm till the party was over.

The parents had such a beautiful time that they decided thereafter to take frequent jaunts around the world.

"Isn't it lovely being tourists, papa?" said Scootles.

Kewpieville

By ROSE O'NEILL

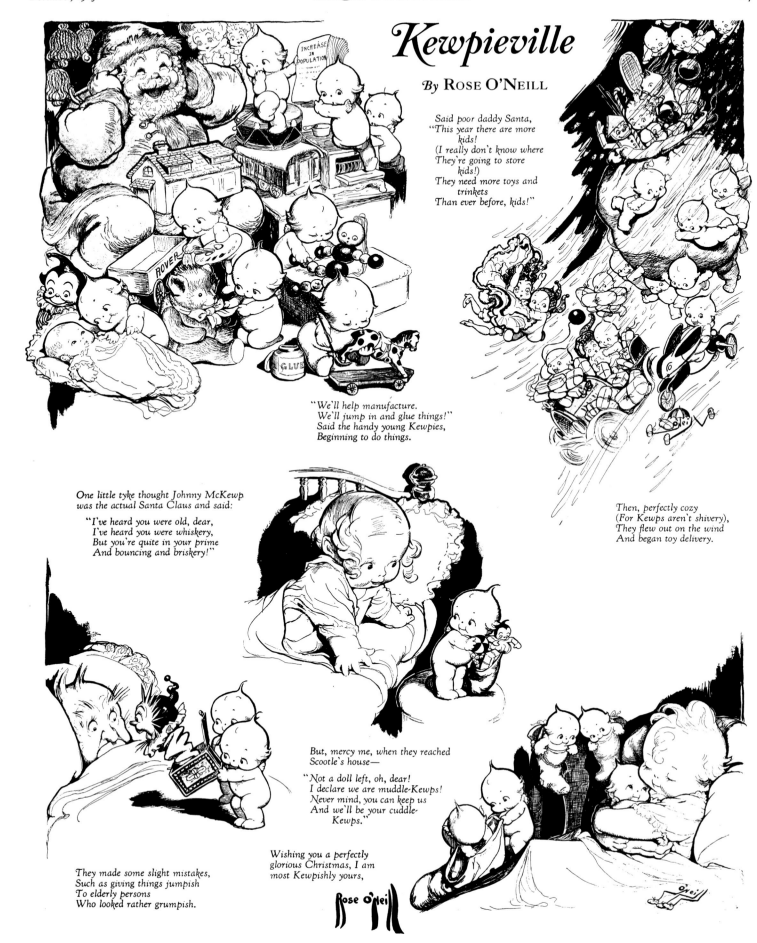

Said poor daddy Santa,
"This year there are more
　　kids!
(I really don't know where
They're going to store
　　kids!)
They need more toys and
　　trinkets
Than ever before, kids!"

"We'll help manufacture.
We'll jump in and glue things!"
Said the handy young Kewpies,
Beginning to do things.

One little tyke thought Johnny McKewp
was the actual Santa Claus and said:

"I've heard you were old, dear,
I've heard you were whiskery,
But you're quite in your prime
And bouncing and briskery!"

Then, perfectly cozy
(For Kewps aren't shivery),
They flew out on the wind
And began toy delivery.

But, mercy me, when they reached
Scootle's house—

"Not a doll left, oh, dear!
I declare we are muddle-Kewps!
Never mind, you can keep us
And we'll be your cuddle-
　　Kewps."

Wishing you a perfectly
glorious Christmas, I am
most Kewpishly yours,

They made some slight mistakes,
Such as giving things jumpish
To elderly persons
Who looked rather grumpish.

Rose O'Neill

Kewpieville

By Rose O'Neill

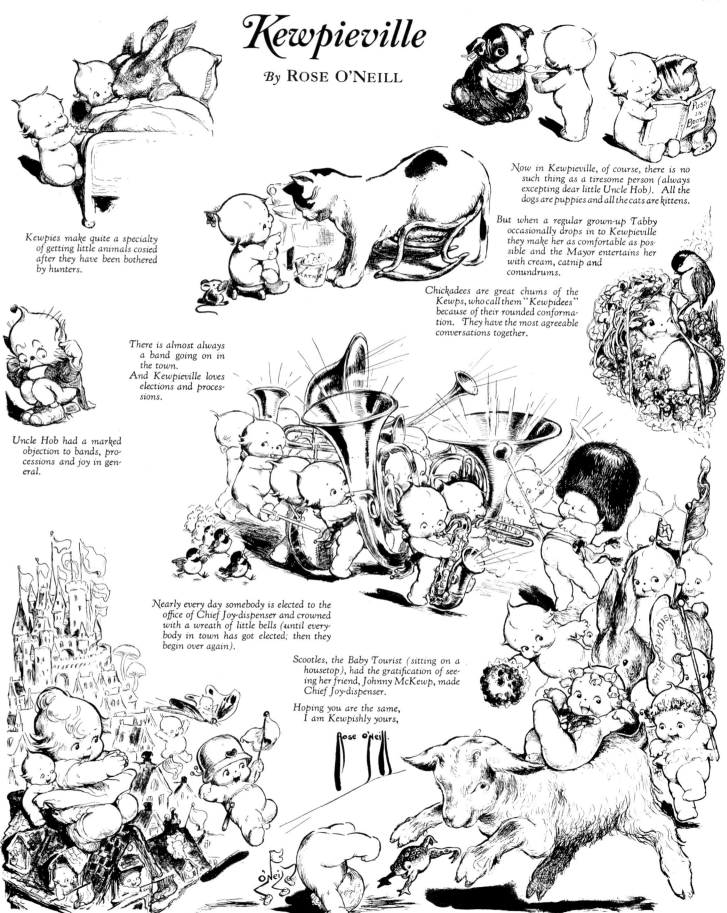

Kewpies make quite a specialty of getting little animals cosied after they have been bothered by hunters.

Uncle Hob had a marked objection to bands, processions and joy in general.

There is almost always a band going on in the town. And Kewpieville loves elections and processions.

Nearly every day somebody is elected to the office of Chief Joy-dispenser and crowned with a wreath of little bells (until everybody in town has got elected; then they begin over again).

Now in Kewpieville, of course, there is no such thing as a tiresome person (always excepting dear little Uncle Hob). All the dogs are puppies and all the cats are kittens.

But when a regular grown-up Tabby occasionally drops in to Kewpieville they make her as comfortable as possible and the Mayor entertains her with cream, catnip and conundrums.

Chickadees are great chums of the Kewps, who call them "Kewpidees" because of their rounded conformation. They have the most agreeable conversations together.

Scootles, the Baby Tourist (sitting on a housetop), had the gratification of seeing her friend, Johnny McKewp, made Chief Joy-dispenser.

Hoping you are the same, I am Kewpishly yours,

Rose O'Neill

Kewpieville

By Rose O'Neill

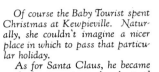

Of course the Baby Tourist spent Christmas at Kewpieville. Naturally, she couldn't imagine a nicer place in which to pass that particular holiday.

As for Santa Claus, he became perfectly uproarious when he paid a business call at the Kewpieville Hotel. The picture at the left will tell you why. He found the biggest hotel cradle full to overflowing, with a stocking bountifully filled and thoughtfully labeled "For Santa."

Every Kewpieville home was well tidied up for Christmas. Kewpieville doesn't have vacuum cleaners, to be sure, but Tinker Bell never floated up and down a wall any better than a really well-bred Kewpie, so vacuum cleaners aren't missed.

Santa Claus was invited to spend the whole day in Kewpieville with his Package Elf—the one that always does up the Christmas parcels. The Elf wasn't very much used to good society (being only a simple Package Elf), so he giggled a good deal at being entertained. A real sofa was provided; and Santa said he'd never had so much attention and certainly did enjoy it, particularly the family album.

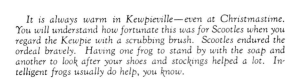

It is always warm in Kewpieville—even at Christmastime. You will understand how fortunate this was for Scootles when you regard the Kewpie with a scrubbing brush. Scootles endured the ordeal bravely. Having one frog to stand by with the soap and another to look after your shoes and stockings helped a lot. Intelligent frogs usually do help, you know.

Kewpieville

By ROSE O'NEILL

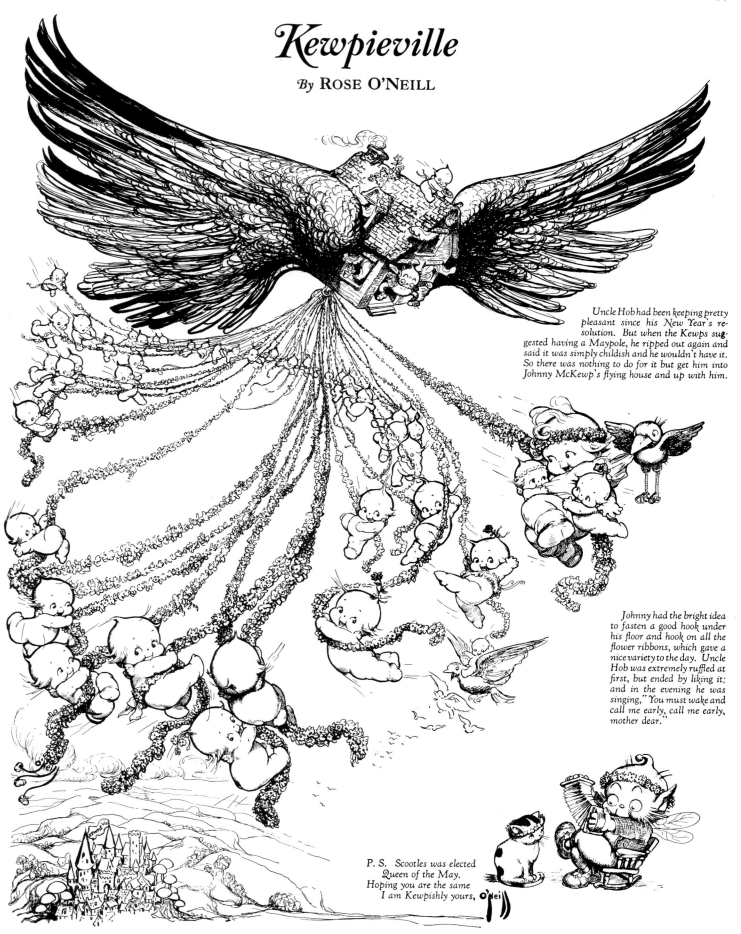

Uncle Hob had been keeping pretty pleasant since his New Year's resolution. But when the Kewps suggested having a Maypole, he ripped out again and said it was simply childish and he wouldn't have it. So there was nothing to do for it but get him into Johnny McKewp's flying house and up with him.

Johnny had the bright idea to fasten a good hook under his floor and hook on all the flower ribbons, which gave a nice variety to the day. Uncle Hob was extremely ruffled at first, but ended by liking it; and in the evening he was singing, "You must wake and call me early, call me early, mother dear."

P. S. Scootles was elected Queen of the May. Hoping you are the same I am Kewpishly yours, O'Neill

JOSEPH KALLUS
The Interpreter of Kewpie

Illustration 8. Joseph L. Kallus with vinyl *Kewpies* at Toy Fair, 1953.

Rose O'Neill's saucy little Kewpie became so popular after the first illustrations appeared in magazines in 1909 that there was a demand to manufacture commercial items bearing the Kewpie likeness. A market developed for books, comic strips, lamps, dishes, postcards, figurines, dolls, jewelry and many other kinds of merchandise items. Rose O'Neill would not have been able to produce all the models and samples that mass merchandising would require. One of the first distributors to show an interest in the Kewpie properties was Geo. Borgfeldt & Co.

In 1881 Geo. Borgfeldt & Co. was formed as a partnership with George Borgfeldt, Marcell Kahle and Joseph L. Kahle. The purpose of the firm was to import from Europe dolls, toys, figurines and novelty items for distribution to the American market. Branch offices were established in New York City, in Canada and all over

Europe, particularly in Germany, the center of the doll and toy manufacturing industry. George Borgfeldt resigned as president of the firm in 1900 and was succeeded by Marcell Kahle. After the death of Kahle in 1909, Fred Kolb became president. In 1912 Kolb entered negotiations with Rose O'Neill to produce a variety of *Kewpie* figurines and dolls. They decided to hire an American assistant to render designs from Rose O'Neill's drawings of Kewpie.

An advertisement for a sculptor was sent to the Fine Arts College of Pratt Institute in Brooklyn and a 17-year-old student, Joseph L. Kallus, of Brooklyn, applied for the position and was interviewed by Kolb and O'Neill. Kallus made some rough modeling sketches from O'Neill's drawings and was hired to execute *Kewpies* for manufacture in Germany. It has always been a practice in the doll industry for a designer (in this case Rose O'Neill) to initiate the idea for a doll and to establish a rough perimeter of the conceived product and to obtain assistance in the actual modeling and casting of the doll. Then the original designer offers suggestions, changes and approval of the final product. Kallus worked with O'Neill in designing the first *Kewpie* figurines and dolls that were to be produced in bisque in Germany in several factories with which Borgfeldt was affiliated, among them J.D. Kestner, Gebr. Voight and Herman Voigt. Karl Standfuss made celluloid *Kewpies* and Margarete Steiff made cloth *Kewpies*.

Fred Kolb and Rose O'Neill were delighted with the work that Joseph L. Kallus was completing on the *Kewpie* project. Kolb also retained Kallus to design other dolls while he continued with his studies at Pratt Institute.

Dorothy Gregory Moffett was a fellow art student in the Pratt classes attended by Kallus in 1912. In 1974, during legal proceedings to protect the Kewpie copyrights, Moffett submitted an affidavit in which she told about the first time she saw the *Kewpie* dolls:

"Mr. Kallus brought three Kewpie doll heads to class, and he passed them around and explained the work he was doing on them. This demonstration occurred in the Max Herman illustration class.

I did not know at the time of the demonstration that these were Kewpie dolls. I knew only that they were different from the dolls we were used to seeing. They had no hair, but they had a small topknot on a symetrically round head to depict the caricature of a child, which distinguished them from anything that I had ever seen in dolls. It was not until I saw Kewpie illustrations published in Good Housekeeping Magazine, Ladies' Home Journal (sic) and other periodicals that I came to know that the dolls which Mr. Kallus had demonstrated to the class were the original sculptures of illustrations drawn and originally conceived by Rose O'Neill from which Kewpie dolls were made.

My clear recollection is that the doll heads which Mr. Kallus demonstrated to the class at that time were handmade samples in plaster of Paris. Mr. Kallus explained to the instructor (Max Herman) the work he had done on those heads and asked for comment and criticism. I was quite interested in this incident and have retained a recollection of it over the years.

...To the best of my knowledge and belief, Mr. Kallus and I are the sole surviving students of that class."

Doll design gave Joseph L. Kallus a career that he had not considered when he first entered Pratt Institute on a scholarship. The bisque dolls and figurines of Kewpie were probably produced in Germany during 1912, 1913 and 1914 and likely again in the 1920s after World War I. In 1916 Kallus himself founded the Rex Doll Co. to produce composition *Kewpie* dolls, as supplies from Germany were halted by the war. These dolls were distributed by Borgfeldt, who controlled all production rights to *Kewpie* dolls and figurines. With permission from Borgfeldt, the Rex Doll Co. also made a line of composition *Kewpie*

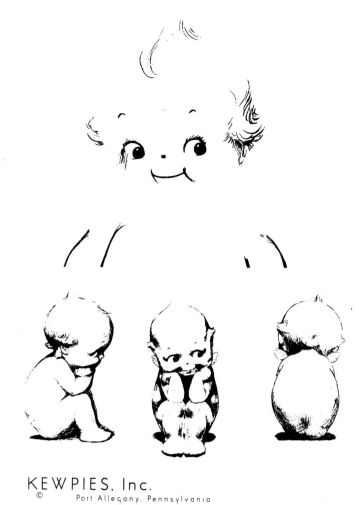

KEWPIES, Inc.
© Port Allegany, Pennsylvania

Illustration 9. Kewpie drawings by Joseph L. Kallus.

The Spirit of KEWPIES ©

Illustration 10. *The Spirit of Kewpies,* probably drawn by Joseph L. Kallus.

Illustration 11. Fourteen Kewpies hanging on a clothes line, probably drawn by Joseph L. Kallus.

dolls that were distributed by the Tip Top Toy Co., a distributor of carnival prizes. (It must be remembered that carnival prizes were a much higher grade of merchandise in 1916 than they are today.)

In 1918 Kallus received the first of many copyrights on his own doll designs. His first character doll was *Baby Bundie*. That year, at about age 24, Kallus attempted to secure an assignment for the war effort. He had several of his instructors at Pratt Institute, among them Frederick T. Baker and O.W. Beck, and Frank Vincent DuMond, an instructor at the Art Students' League of New York (where Kallus had also studied), submit letters of reference to Charles Dana Gibson, the famous illustrator and creator of the "Gibson Girl," who was Chairman of Pictorial Publicity in New York for the war effort. Instead, Kallus trained for fire observation during World War I.

From 1919 to 1921 Kallus was President of the Mutual Doll Co., a firm that made composition *Kewpies*; *Baby Bundie* dolls; and *Bo-Fair*, *Dollie* and *Vanitie*, who had specially designed socket joints. Kallus resigned from Mutual in 1921.

In 1922 Kallus established the Cameo Doll Co., which lasted in one form or another until 1982 when Kallus assigned all his properties to Jesco, Inc. Most of the dolls and animals made by Cameo until after World War II were of composition and segmented wood joints. For Borgfeldt Cameo made *Kewpies* and introduced the Kallus designs *Baby Bo Kaye* and *Little Annie Rooney*. Little Annie Rooney was the creation of Jack Collins who wrote and illustrated comic strips for newspapers. Little Annie Rooney was made as an all-bisque figure and as a fully-jointed composition doll.

The Cameo Doll Products Company was located in Port Allegheny, Pennsylvania, from 1933 until 1968, when the molds for dolls were taken over by the Strombecker Corporation of Chicago. In October 1934 a fire almost devastated the entire plant during its busiest season.

After rebuilding, Cameo also manufactured dolls for other doll companies, who packaged them in boxes with their own company names, most notably the Effanbee Doll Corporation while it was owned by Noma Electric in the late 1940s.

In 1933 Kallus was summoned to Washington by President Roosevelt as a representative of small industrial firms in Pennsylvania. He consulted with the President to suggest the most feasible methods of bringing the depression economy back to normal production.

After Rose O'Neill died in 1944, the rights to produce *Kewpie*, *Scootles* and *Ho-Ho* were granted to Joseph Kallus in an indirect manner. Before her death, Rose O'Neill had attempted to transfer the rights for her creations to Kallus. (It has been suggested that there was a romantic relationship between Kallus and O'Neill, but no proof of this assertion has been established.) In 1947 all trademark, patent and copyright rights to Kewpie were assigned to Joseph Kallus by John Hugh O'Neill, Rose's nephew and heir. John Hugh O'Neill renewed the copyright for the book *Kewpie and the Runaway Baby* in 1955 and Kallus later requested from O'Neill's wife that these rights be assigned to him as he wanted "to protect the good will and name of Rose O'Neill and her Kewpie creation." It is not clear at what time Kallus obtained the rights to other O'Neill properties such as *Scootles* and *Ho-Ho*, or if money changed hands for these rights.

Mr. Kallus spent a great deal of his energy in his later years licensing the Kewpie designs and entering litigation with the various firms to whom he had licensed the right to produce Kewpie and other O'Neill designs. In 1976, at age 83, Kallus suffered a great personal and professional loss when thieves entered his basement in Brooklyn and stole a large amount of original *Kewpie* models and designs. Patent materials had also been stolen from two safes that were in the basement. The police did not understand the value of these works. Detective Robert

Hall of the 67th Precinct said to the *New York Times* reporter, "The dolls were probably handmade and looked pretty, with pretty clothes." Kallus claimed that many of his original models of *Kewpie*, the original *Scootles*, his handmade *Joy*, his version of Disney's *Mickey Mouse*, the originals of *Howdy Doody, Superman* and *Pinocchio* were also gone forever. Imagine how valuable these models would be today for a collectors' museum!

In 1960 Kallus had approached the American Character Doll Co. in an effort to have that firm produce *Kewpies* under license to Cameo. American Character was not able to deal with Kallus' blunt style after he accused the company of attempting to copy some of his original concepts. He was answered with a curt note: "I have received your letter of the 24th and am now convinced that your unmitigated gall is only surpassed by your insufferable ego." This was during a time period when other doll companies, particularly those in the Orient, were plagarizing Rose O'Neill and Joseph Kallus *Kewpie* designs and he was trying to protect the rights that he had gained from the O'Neill estate.

In 1969 Strombecker of Chicago began producing *Kewpie* dolls under license to Kallus and Cameo and encouraged him to permit Hallmark Cards Incorporated to produce greeting cards using Rose O'Neill's artwork because it would help promote interest in Kewpie, which had become more popular than it had been for many years. In 1972 Knickerbocker Toy Co., Inc. approached Kallus for permission to license any characters that were controlled by Cameo. A contract was awarded to Knickerbocker but Kallus also made an agreement with Kutsuwa Co., Ltd., of Osaka, Japan, to license several Kewpie properties. In 1973 Milton Bradley, Inc., under the Amsco division of the company, began to manufacture *Kewpies* in vinyl. Strombecker and Cameo had terminated their licensing agreement in 1973 because Kallus was not granted the privilege of approving all samples of the dolls that Strombecker would produce. This antagonized Joseph Kallus, who wanted to maintain high standards for the Rose O'Neill designs that he owned according to the contact between Cameo and Strombecker. By 1976 Milton Bradley had severed its association with Joseph Kallus over conflicts in royalty payments and the fact that the company did not mark its doll packages in accordance with its contract with Kallus.

Again in 1980 Kallus tried to interest Knickerbocker in the *Kewpie* dolls, but the company was afraid to deal with him after it was known that he had problems with Strombecker and Milton Bradley, which were assumed to be more the fault of an aging and irascible Kallus than of the doll companies. By 1980 it was becoming more and more difficult to protect Kewpie copyrights from infringements, as unscrupulous individuals were printing Kewpie postcards and other Kewpie likenesses and making dolls that looked like Kewpie and selling these things on an individual basis to collectors. All of this could cause potential problems to those who wanted to manufacture

Illustrations 12. and 13. A self-portrait of Joseph L. Kallus and a portrait of his wife, described by Kallus as "quick rough portraits."

Illustrations 14, 15 and 16. Paintings by Joseph L. Kallus, probably from his later years.

My dear Joe,

You must have been thinking me a perfect brute not to have written to you about the catastrophe. The truth is, I was so flabbergasted, it seemed I couldn't pull myself together to speak of it. I've written you every day in my mind, and felt the greatest sympathy for your misfortune — after your heroic efforts and your achievement of a truly beautiful irresistable thing.

As for me, I feel like a convict that felt himself nearing the end of his term, only to learn he has another twenty years. You and I are both starving to get to the life of artists, so we can understand each other's sufferings.

I don't ask a letter from you now. You must be almost frantic. But when you come you will tell me if there are any elements of hope — if the Scootles moulds achieved with such time and difficulty — were not all destroyed. And if you will, now, move your industry back near New York.

We have just finished two Scootles books for Saalfield (ten cent store trade) one, "Scootles in Kewpieville", a book with a story of Scootles for children to colour and with a drawing lesson by me. The other a cut-out Scootles paper doll book with one big Scootles and two small on the cover, with Kewpies — and dresses inside.

I am falling behind with my Syndicate Page, but as quickly as possible I shall prepare the figures for your jewelry and paper articles. Mr. Marks brought me your designs.

And now my dear Joe let me send you my belated, but most heartfelt sorrow and a thousand hopes that the future will make you full amends.

Faithfully yours,

Rose

Callista joins me in this message.

106 West 13th Street
Chelsea 3. 6614

1935

Illustration 17. A three-page letter from Rose O'Neill to Joseph L. Kallus, 1935. The letter is expressing O'Neill's dismay over the fire that nearly destroyed the Cameo Doll Company in October 1934. Rose O'Neill wrote all of her letters in this style, preferring printing over longhand.

genuine *Kewpie* dolls and who wanted to protect their rights and licenses.

By the 1980s Joseph Kallus could have sold the rights to Kewpie to any of several major American doll companies who wanted them. He chose Nancy Villaseñor of Jesco, Inc.

In 1982 Nancy Villaseñor, the President of Jesco, met with Joseph L. Kallus to discuss the Kewpie properties. Villaseñor was inspired in this decision by her partner, Jim Skahill, the Vice President of Jesco. Skahill had a toy and import business in California and he imported such doll lines as Italocremona, Migliorati, Corolle, CR Club and about 20 others. In 1971 he hired Nancy Villaseñor, shortly after she graduated from U.C.L.A., to act as a sales representative to sell dolls from the lines imported from Europe, and dolls from some American companies.

While working in the import business Nancy became exposed to many of the "better" dolls, and of all the toy companies that she represented and sold for, dolls became her chief interest. She was convinced by Skahill to begin to manufacture dolls for a company that she would found.

In the spring of 1982 Nancy went to New York to meet with Joseph Kallus, then age 89, to discuss licensing arrangements for making *Kewpie* dolls. Kallus saw in Nancy a person who would do with Kewpie as he had done. He said that he was not as interested in making money at his age as he was in continuing the traditions of excellence that had always been associated with Kewpie and with Cameo and he thought that Nancy would do this. Kallus agreed to assign all the rights to Kewpie and all the rights to Cameo designs to Nancy Villaseñor when he realized that her business goals equaled his: She was committed to developing a business based on quality toys for the quality toy market.

After Kallus and Villaseñor had concluded the initial part of their business arrangement, he was injured in a traffic accident and died suddenly. Rita Abraham, Kallus' daughter who had no interest in her father's designs, met with Nancy Villaseñor when she went to New York to supervise the transportation to California of the original *Kewpie* and Cameo doll molds. Mrs. Abraham wanted Nancy to have the 21 trunks of Cameo dolls, clothing patterns, and Rose O'Neill artwork that Mr. Kallus had stored in his apartment, along with many boxes of files and business records.

Villaseñor's first *Kewpies*, released in 1983, were a re-issue of the 27 inch (69cm) *Kewpie* of 1966; "Yesterday's Kewpie," a 16 inch (41cm) dressed in outfits from the past; and "Kewpie Goes...," a 12 inch (31cm) series in various theme-oriented clothing designs.

The re-issued *Kewpie* from 1966 for collectors as made by Jesco is slightly smaller than the original version. This is because the older version was made from a stock body and legs, whereas the *Kewpie* made by Jesco is cast from Kallus' original molds. Nancy Villaseñor reported that, "It would have been more cost effective to make new molds, but we were committed to using the original molds as we promised Joseph Kallus."

The series of 16 inch (41cm) *Kewpies* are modeled after the designs that Cameo issued in 1961. The 12 inch (31cm) designs have clothing designed by Shirley Pepys. These *Kewpies* also meet with the objectives of Kallus and Villaseñor: "To make *Kewpie* available for the enjoyment of children and to satisfy the *Kewpie* hunger of collectors."

Nancy Villaseñor and Jim Skahill have given up much of their European product import company to concentrate on developing and manufacturing Cameo designs from Joseph L. Kallus. Their dolls are manufactured in California, from American components. Jesco promised to pursue two directions relating to Cameo dolls. These are 1.) To make original Cameo dolls with the original Cameo molds. 2.) To develop new Cameo dolls, continuing the tradition of Joseph Kallus. Doll design, development and manufacture will expand in both areas. Jesco does not take any shortcuts, such as using cheaper blow-molded doll bodies. Jesco's attitude is that its growth pattern should be for "better dolls," not for "more dolls."

Doll collectors and children of all ages are delighted that *Kewpie* is back again — and back to stay at Jesco.

Illustration 19. *The Kewpies Their Book*, published by Frederick A. Stokes Company, 1911. This large format book has a hard cover and is 80 pages. Both the verse and pictures of this book and similar books were by Rose O'Neill. *Joyce Stafford Collection.*

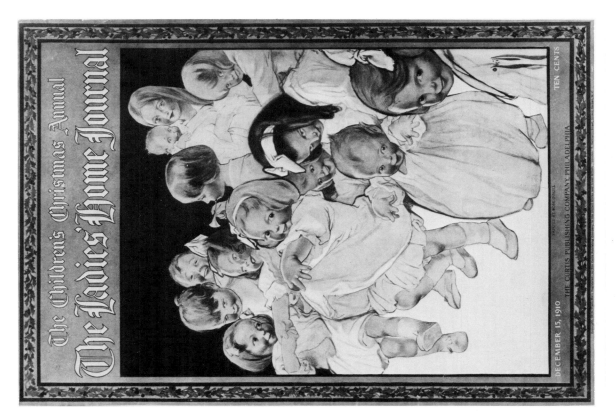

Illustration 18. Rose O'Neill illustration for the December 15, 1910, cover of *The Ladies' Home Journal. Author's Collection.*

The following illustrations are from *The Kewpies Their Book*, 1911. These Rose O'Neill illustrations show the range of her imagination and the clever poses in which she placed the Kewpies. The pictures in the book were printed in black and white with pink and red coloring. *Joyce Stafford Collection.*

6 *The Kewpies and Their New Adventures*

8

As watering makes flowers grow,
The child treats all their winglets so.
The Kewps submit, and thank her so much,
Though Kewpish wings can never grow much.

Illustration 21. The poor child is watering the wings of the Kewpies because she thinks that it will make them grow.

"They make her pale cheeks pink with flowers"

Illustration 20. The Kewpies and a poor child that they found "in an alley, poor and small."

12.

And when 'twas time for her to go,
Dot and the baby hugged her so.
And then the Kewps took her away, dears,
But brought her back another day, dears.

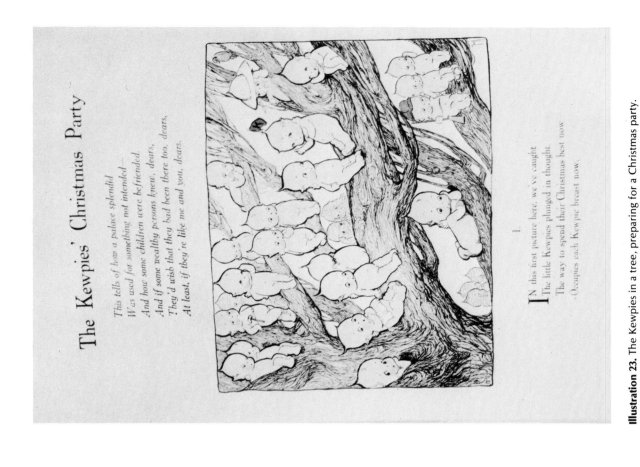

The Kewpies' Christmas Party

This tells of how a palace splendid
Was used for something not intended—
And how some children were befriended
And if some wealthy persons knew, dears,
They'd wish that they had been there too, dears,
At least, if they're like me and you, dears.

I.

IN this first picture here, we've caught
The little Kewpies plunged in thought
The way to spend their Christmas best now
Occupies each Kewpie breast now.

Illustration 22. The Kewpies present the poor child to Dottie Darling.

Illustration 23. The Kewpies in a tree, preparing for a Christmas party.

4.

"It's all so nice," said she, "but oh,
My washing can't be finished so!"
"Just take a nap," the Kewps said, winking,
"We'll see to that as quick as thinking."

21.

And really, they were right, you see,
Such circuses can't often be.
At least, there will be room for us, I think,
Till Kewpies grow more numerous, I think.

22.

And Charles and Claribelle McGee,
No happier children could you see!
The Kewps give good advice for thanks, my dears:
"Henceforth you'd better mind your banks, my dears."

ABOVE: Illustration 24. The Kewpies washing the clothes of Mrs. Jane McGraw, "a sadder sight you ever saw! A dreadful cold, rheumatic shoulder, Baby crying, weather colder."

16.

No sooner said than done, the band
Take up the basket out of hand;
The baby laughs at Kewpish jiggling,
His little legs go briskly wiggling.

17.

What this last picture shows, you see:
Miss Mary Dole all smiles and glee!
The Kewpies have succeeded there;
'Twas just the thing she needed, there.

ABOVE: Illustration 25. The Kewpies at the circus.

Illustration 26. The Kewpies and Miss Mary Dole, "the Poor Old Soul" whom they cheered up by bringing an abandoned baby which " 'Twas just the thing she needed, there."

Illustrations 27, 28 and 29. Four pages from *Good Housekeeping*, 1915, telling about the Kewpie's pet, the Kewpie dog. *Author's Collection.*

He started off with it most helpfully,
And 'stead of thanks, she chased him yelpfully!

This so upset his equanimity,
It so disturbed his soul's sublimity.

That over him there crept a droop-
ishness
That made him long for Home—and
Kewpishness!

A bulldog's fearsome at his happiest.
Words can't describe him at his scrap-
piest.
With battling eye, triumphant braggi-
ness,
And utter lack of pleasant wagginess.

The poor, scared Kewpidoodle smiled
at him,
Which made that bulldog simply wild
at him.
"Am I the sport of you riffraff!" he
roared:
"Am I that sight that makes dogs
laugh?" he roared.

The Kewpidoodle's
intentions were
so kindly.

Well, dears, a cloud of Kewpies smoth-
ered him
With answers soft. They soothed
and mothered him.
"Sir Dog," they crooned, "don't be so
iresome.
For wrath's unhealthful, hot, and
tiresome!"

The Kewpidoodle, gay but
sheepish, too,
Hilarious, but feeling
cheapish, too,
Heard Ducky Daddles
loudly snickering,
And saw the Kewpish
dimples flickering.
They weren't cross, they
weren't cool to him
They simply
mentioned
"April Fool"
to him!

A bulldog's fearsome at his
happiest.
Words can't describe him
at his scrappiest.

"I only smiled at him," said the Kewpidoodle.

Illustration 31. 11¾ inch (30cm) cardboard stand-up advertisement featuring Kewpie with a red flocked Santa Claus hat advertising Kewpie embroidery pictures, probably pre-1920. *Helen Sieverling Collection.*

They Wanted
Jell-O

Do you remember the dreadful disappointment it used to be in the old days at home when mother brought on for dessert some baked apples or pieplant pie, or something else that was too common, and you had expected ice cream or shortcake at least?

Now the little folks want Jell-O, and it is so delicious, refreshing, pure and wholesome, so "economical" and so easily prepared, that there is no reason why the little tots or anybody else should be disappointed in their dessert.

Creamy Desserts

That do not require any cream at all for making them, nor eggs or sugar, are made in perfection of Jell-O—and of course they do not have to be cooked.

To give you the best possible idea of "the Jell-O way" we will send you, free, a copy of the latest Jell-O Book, which gives full information on the subject, if you will send us your name and address.

In every case of sickness or convalescence there is a period when feeding is a most important factor, and often it is found that Jell-O is the one particular dish which satisfies the craving for something refreshing and revives the weakened appetite.

Jell-O is made in six pure fruit flavors: Strawberry, Raspberry, Lemon, Orange, Cherry, Chocolate. At any grocer's, 2 packages for **25 cents.**

THE GENESEE PURE FOOD COMPANY,
Le Roy, N. Y., and Bridgeburg, Ont.

Illustration 30. Page advertisement from *Pictorial Review*, March 1919, with Rose O'Neill art promoting Jell-O. Rose O'Neill's art featuring Kewpie touted Jell-O for many years. *Author's Collection.*

Kewpieville

Verse and Drawings by ROSE O'NEILL

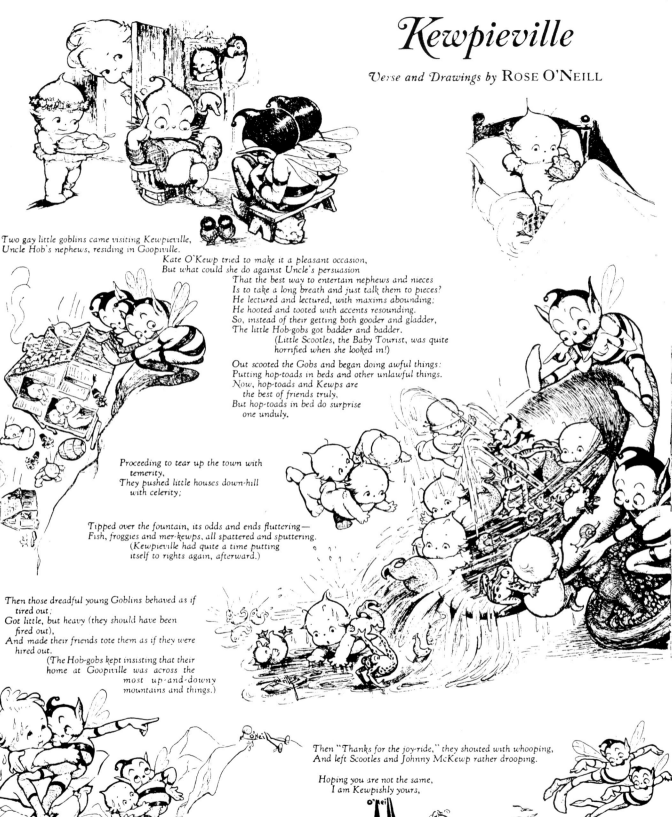

Two gay little goblins came visiting Kewpieville,
Uncle Hob's nephews, residing in Goopiville.

Kate O'Kewp tried to make it a pleasant occasion,
But what could she do against Uncle's persuasion
That the best way to entertain nephews and nieces
Is to take a long breath and just talk them to pieces?
He lectured and lectured, with maxims abounding;
He hooted and tooted with accents resounding.
So, instead of their getting both gooder and gladder,
The little Hob-gobs got badder and badder.
   (Little Scootles, the Baby Tourist, was quite
   horrified when she looked in!)

Out scooted the Gobs and began doing awful things:
Putting hop-toads in beds and other unlawful things.
Now, hop-toads and Kewps are
  the best of friends truly,
But hop-toads in bed do surprise
  one unduly.

Proceeding to tear up the town with
  temerity,
They pushed little houses down-hill
  with celerity;

Tipped over the fountain, its odds and ends fluttering—
Fish, froggies and mer-kewps, all spattered and sputtering.
  (Kewpieville had quite a time putting
  itself to rights again, afterward.)

Then those dreadful young Goblins behaved as if
  tired out;
Got little, but heavy (they should have been
  fired out),
And made their friends tote them as if they were
  hired out.
   (The Hob-gobs kept insisting that their
   home at Goopiville was across the
     most up-and-downy
     mountains and things.)

Then "Thanks for the joy-ride," they shouted with whooping,
And left Scootles and Johnny McKewp rather drooping.

Hoping you are not the same,
  I am Kewpishly yours,

Illustration 32. Page from *The Ladies' Home Journal*, October 1925.

Illustration 34. American Greetings card, copyrighted by Joseph Kallus, 1973, featuring original Rose O'Neill artwork.

Illustration 33. Kewpies comic book, a Will Eisner Production, Spring 1949, copyrighted by Joseph Kallus.

The Time To Be Happy Is Now

The time to be happy is right now--today!
Nothing's forever, you know
And life's awfully short to be wasted away
With fretting and fussing
...and so
I look for the people whose faces say "love"
And who "live a lot" all their lives through
Those are the people I want to be like
And *their* happy makes *me* happy, too!

Having fun is nicer
Than NOT having fun, you know
And having fun TOGETHER
Is two times the fun — and so

That's how come being friends is nice —
A friend's someone to share with
To laugh with... and to say things to —
To like — and go somewhere with!

And if I had to choose ONE thing
I thought was THE most fun
I'd choose a FRIEND — and cross my heart
YOU would be the one!

ABOVE LEFT and RIGHT: Illustrations 35 and 36. Large format American Greetings cards, copyright 1973 by Joseph L. Kallus and featuring original Rose O'Neill artwork.

ABOVE and RIGHT: Illustrations 37 and 38. Unauthorized postcards sold commercially in the 1970s featuring original Rose O'Neill artwork. These cards and several similar ones were produced in full color. *Author's Collection.*

PART II

KEWPIES FOR COLLECTORS

KEWPIES FOR COLLECTORS

In 1912 Geo. Borgfeldt & Co. of New York City had obtained the right to manufacture three-dimensional likenesses of Rose O'Neill's Kewpie and Joseph L. Kallus was hired to sculpt and develop figurines and dolls of Kewpie from Rose O'Neill's original drawings. It is the usual procedure in these arrangements for the company who will wholesale the product to develop certain types of products that it thinks will have a wide retail market. It is difficult for collectors of memorabilia and the charming artifacts from the past to realize that the only reason that these things were made was to make money. Kewpies as figurines and dolls were not the creative expression of Rose O'Neill; she created the original ideas as illustrations and for the three-dimensional works she received a minimum royalty for each *Kewpie* item that was sold. *Kewpies* were sold in the thousands, if not in the millions, so Miss O'Neill earned a lot of money from the production of the figurines and dolls that Borgfeldt distributed to retailers. Joseph L. Kallus was probably paid a salary or a fee for each *Kewpie* item that he created from the O'Neill drawings. (For his own designs he would be in a position to receive a royalty.) Miss O'Neill may have had the right to approve all designs executed by Kallus and placed into production by Borgfeldt but it is unlikely that she constantly exercised them after the initial stages of the business agreements between herself, Borgfeldt and Kallus, during which time she had approved the first Kallus' *Kewpie* samples.

The most plausible process for transferring Rose O'Neill's drawings into completed figurines and products would follow this course: The Borgfeldt company would determine that there was a market for a certain style of figurine. Principals within the company would then look over Rose O'Neill's drawings and illustrations from published and unpublished sources and decide to produce an item such as the *Kewpie Traveler*. Kallus would be commissioned to sculpt a *Kewpie Traveler*. The first rendering would be in clay. From this a model could be cast or a plaster mold could be made (in two parts) from the clay model. For bisque and porcelain production the original molds are usually made of plaster of paris. (Metal molds were also made from which to create additional plaster molds.) Liquid porcelain slip is poured into the mold from the opening in the bottom. The plaster mold absorbs some of the water from the slip and the remaining part retains a slightly firm shape when it is released from the mold. Then the cast portion is cleaned and smoothed so that mold lines do not show; additional features, such as a flower, are applied to the pliable "green ware," and the finished figure is baked in a kiln at a very high temperature so that it will assume a hardened and permanent form. Then the figure is painted and decorated and the coloring is fired or "cooked" into the figurine. Mass-produced bisque or porcelain figures from the early years of the 20th century for the "better market" were given a "high firing," at a very high temperature, which produced a harder and smoother finish, but which caused more loss in the firing process as some items would crack, bend or lose the proper shape. Most mass-produced porcelain and bisque figurines that are meant to sell for a low cost today are given a "low firing," which causes less kiln loss but produces a product that is rougher to the touch and which can fracture or break more easily if it is dropped or receives a blow from another object. A low firing also saves time in production. Most porcelain production for the mass market that was meant to sell at a reasonable price during the early years of the 20th century was completed in Germany, the "Taiwan of its day."

Germany was not formed as one nation until 1871 and it began to industrialize very quickly afterwards. Wages in Germany were low and workers were abundant. Hundreds of porcelain-making factories had already been operating in the German states and they continued to fill the demand for porcelain products, such as figurines and dolls for markets abroad, principally in the United States, which had a large middle class with more money to spend for children's toys than any other country at the time, with the possible exception of Great Britain, which had a smaller population. A great percentage of these German porcelain factories were located in southern Germany in the historic region of Thüringia. Porcelain production for the manufacture of figurines and dolls was concentrated in the area near Sonneberg, which is

2½ inch (6cm) *Kewpie* place card holder that hangs on a cup and a boutonniere of the same size. *Lillian Rohaly Collection.*

All-bisque *Kewpie* dolls from Germany. Only the arms are jointed and each is incised on the bottom: ''O'NEILL.'' The sizes are 5 inches (13cm). 6¼ inches (16cm) and 10 inches (25cm) tall. *Wanda Lodwick Collection.*

All-composition *Kewpie* dolls from the late 1940s, made by Cameo; distributed by Noma Electric (Effanbee). The undressed model is 11½ inches (29cm) tall and has jointed arms; the fully-jointed doll in the original rompers is 13 inches (33cm) tall. *Author's Collection.*

All-vinyl *Kewpie* dolls from the early 1970s. The sizes are 6 inches (15cm), 10 inches (25cm) and 14 inches (36cm) tall. *Author's Collection.*

All-cloth *Kewpie* dolls from the 1930s. The smaller one is 11 inches (28cm) tall and was made by King Innovations, Inc. The larger one is 17 inches (43cm) tall and was made by Richard G. Kreuger, Inc. Both have painted mask faces. *Wanda Lodwick Collection.*

Rare 6 inch (15cm) all-bisque *Kewpie* with jointed arms and legs. *Helen Sieverling Collection.*

9 inch (23cm) all-hard plastic *Kewpie, circa 1950s, with jointed arms only.*
Author's Collection.

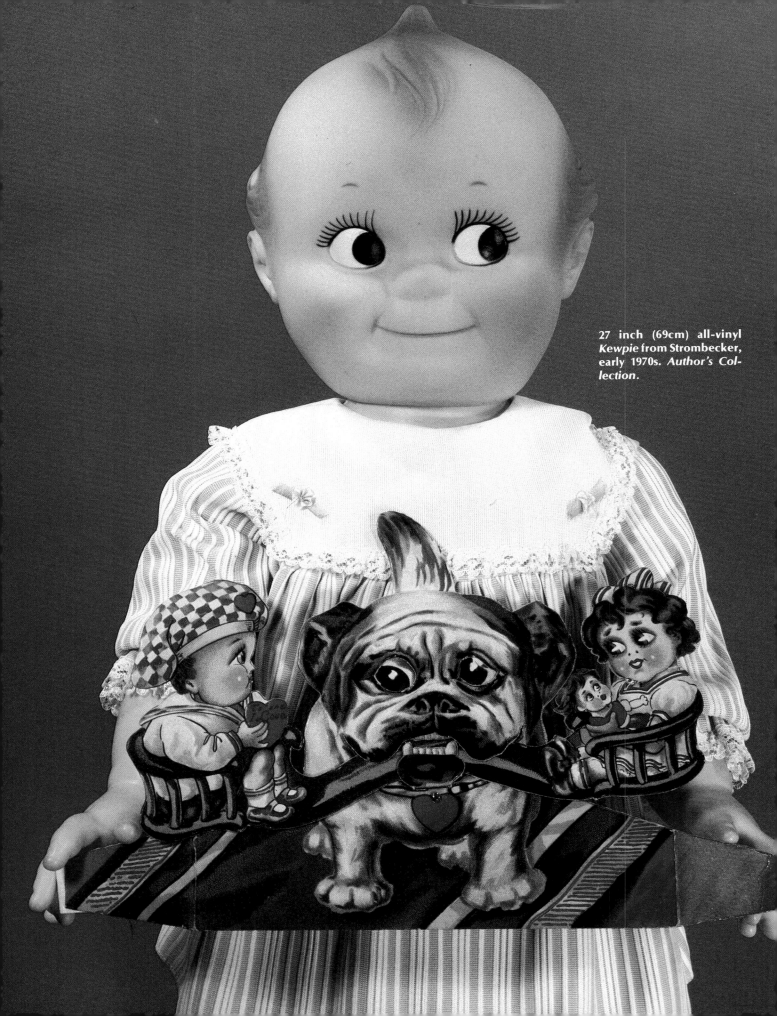

27 inch (69cm) all-vinyl *Kewpie* from Strombecker, early 1970s. *Author's Collection.*

8 inch (20cm) fully-jointed all-vinyl *Kewpie* from Amsco, circa 1973, dressed in an original old-fashioned costume to celebrate Kewpie's 60th birthday. *Author's Collection.*

8 inch (20cm) all-composition and fully-jointed *Scootles*. 1930s. *Patricia N. Schoonmaker Collection.*

now in East Germany near the West German border, and Nuremberg, which is now in West Germany near the East German border. When Geo. Borgfeldt & Co. obtained the rights from Rose O'Neill to manufacture Kewpie in plastic mediums in 1912, most of them were made by the German firm Kestner & Comp. who produced high quality porcelain products at a low price. The average price for an all-bisque *Kewpie* figure or doll before World War I was 15¢, which would roughly translate from $1.00 to $2.00 at today's prices.

It is also highly likely that a low-paid mold maker, who may have considered himself a designer, altered the samples sent to Germany by Borgfeldt and created additional sizes of a design or changed them slightly to produce other variations. It would be simple to change the arm positions of a seated *Kewpie* while it was still in

the "soft" form and place it in various positions that would conform to a figurine that held a dog, a cat or another object. The same seated *Kewpie* in the soft form could be altered slightly to ride a goose, a rocking horse or another animal. Minor changes in production could be approved by Borgfeldt representatives who were located in Germany in the porcelain-producing areas.

The object of *Kewpie* production on an extremely large scale would be to produce various designs that could be quickly turned into figurines that could be made rapidly and immediately dispatched to Borgfeldt in New York who would sell them to other distributors and retailers so that they could reach consumers as soon as possible. *Kewpie* was a "novelty item" and novelty items do not enjoy a long life of permanent production. Thousands of clever and original novelty items have been

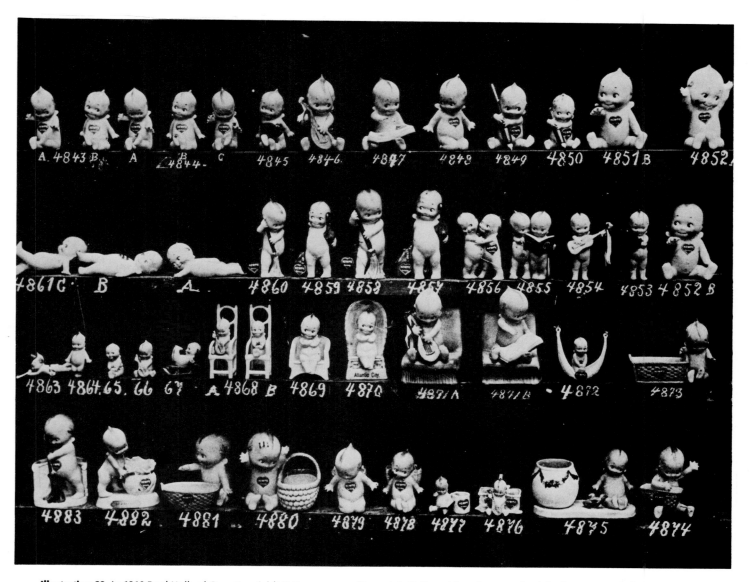

Illustration 39. In 1912 Fred Kolb of Geo. Borgfeldt & Co. presented Joseph L. Kallus with a photograph of the first group of all-bisque *Action Kewpies* from Germany. These were most likely made by Kestner and they range in sizes from 2 inches (5cm) to 5 inches (13cm).

65

made since 1912, but few of them have "withstood the test of time" as Kewpie has, and have become permanent and classic images that are still available for retail sale.

It must also be remembered that a strong reason for Kewpie's continued success was the marketing determination of Joseph L. Kallus. Kallus produced *Kewpies* himself beginning in 1916 and continued to sell or license the image until 1982.

Kewpie in porcelain, bisque and china was made in hundreds of different forms, both as figurines and as dolls. Most of these samples survive today as they were always well thought of. The present price of *Kewpies* made in Germany before World War I is determined by several obvious factors. The rarer items are worth more than the common ones. The common items are usually

simpler designs, showing a single *Kewpie* in a simple standing position; the rarer items are usually ones that are either larger or include other figures with *Kewpie*, like an animal or an object, such as a vase.

The lists on pages 68 and 69 are Rose O'Neill *Kewpie* items that could be classified as figurines, although many of them are now considered "dolls." (Dolls by definition should have some movable parts and should have been originally intended as playthings for children.) The porcelain *Kewpie* figures generally measure from 2 to 5 inches (5 to 13cm). Notable rarities will be cited. These figurines were made in Germany from 1912 to the 1920s; importation was interrupted from about 1915 to 1919 because of World War I.

Illustration 40. 3½ inch (9cm) *Kewpie Traveler* with a black umbrella and a brown suitcase. Marked: "O'NEILL / 4916." *Shirley Buchholz Collection.*

Illustration 41. 3½ inch (9cm) *Kewpie Huggers*, made in Germany. No markings. *Author's Collection.*

ABOVE: Illustration 42. 5½ inch (14cm) *Thinker*, incised "O'NEILL." *Shirley Buchholz Collection.*

RIGHT: Illustration 43. Close-up of the *Thinker*. *Shirley Buchholz Collection.*

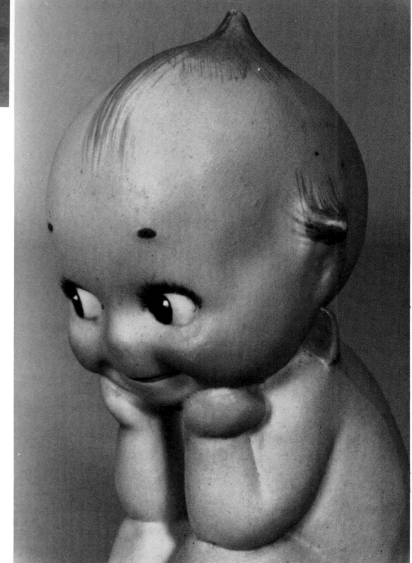

KEWPIE ACTION FIGURES

These are called "action figures" because they present Kewpie in some form of action.

Kewpie positions

Baby with bottle (very rare)
Two babies in a bunting
One Kewpie feeding the other with a spoon from a porridge bowl
Kewpie with hands in the air
Seated and kicking out left leg
Seated and kicking out right leg
Lying on back with feet in the air
Lying on stomach
Polishing boot
Wearing boots
Wearing painted and fired Mary Jane shoes
With molded clothing
Peering out of a basket of flowers

Kewpies that have been given names because of their "Action"

Bather (with sand pail)
Bookworm (seated with book on lap)
Huggers — two Kewpies with arms wrapped around each other — the sizes are usually 3½ inches (9cm), 4 inches (10cm), 5 inches (13cm)
Indian (with molded clothing)
Mother and Child (with large baby bottle)
Readers (two Kewpies with an open book)
Scholar (seated and holding a pen)
Student (wearing glasses and reading a book)
Thinker (One of the most common forms of Kewpie in all media. In porcelain the sizes are from 3 to 6 inches (8 to 15cm), including each half inch size.)
Traveler (carrys an umbrella and a suitcase. Found in every size from 2 inches (5cm) to 5 inches (13cm), including each half inch size.)
Traveler with Kewpie Doodle Dog (much rarer than regular Traveler)

Kewpies that represent some profession

Aviator (with molded binoculars)
Bellhop
Boxer (a variation of the Huggers, but much rarer)
Farmer
Gardner
Golfer
Lawyer
Governor (seated in a chair with crossed arms and legs)
Mayor (seated in a wicker basket chair)
Musician with a drum
Musician with a guitar
Musician with a mandolin
Policeman
Sailor
Soldier:
    wearing a plumed helmet (very rare)
    German soldier coming out of an egg shell (very rare)
    Sitting soldier
    Wounded soldier
    Soldier wearing a Prussian helmet and dressed as a Prussian soldier
    Soldier wearing a "Rough Rider" hat
    Confederate soldier
Sweeper (with a broom)

Kewpie with an animal

Bee on foot
Butterfly in hand
Cat on lap
with two Cats; one is black and one is gray
with a Chicken
with a Chicken coming out of an egg
with a Chicken and a vase full of eggs
with Kewpie Doodle Dog:
    Kewpie lying on his stomach; dog is on his back
    Kewpie and Doodle Dog on a log
    Kewpie seated on Doodle Dog
    Kewpie and Doodle Dog on a bench
    Kewpie and Doodle Dog with an umbrella
    Kewpie and Doodle Dog on a bench; dog is being fed from a bottle
with an Elephant in two versions:
    Elephant is on his back; Kewpie is seated on his stomach
    Elephant is sitting by Kewpie
Fly on Kewpie's toe
riding a Goose
with Rabbit
on Rocking Horse
holding a Teddy Bear
with a Turkey

Kewpie with an object

Basket
Basket on Kewpie's back
in Bath Tub
in Bed
twins in a Blanket (very rare)
with Buckets on a chain
with Yoke and Buckets on a chain
with a cup

Kewpie with an object, continued

on a Chair at a table set with a tea service
with Comb seated in a bath tub
with a Hat and Purse (attached to vase)
holding a Heart
with a Jack-o-Lantern
with Knapsack
with Outhouse
holding a Pen
with Pen and Inkwell
with Potted Plant
wrapped in a Rose
holding a Rose
holding a Rose and seated in a hammock
with flowers attached to a vase
holding a Sack
seated in a Sea Shell
standing on a Sea Shell
with a Shoe
on a Sled
in a Swing
at a Table
on a Tray (holding a pen)

Miscellaneous Kewpie items of bisque

Bottle top attached to a cork
Buttonaire (attaches through a buttonhole)
Buttons
Stick Pin
Place Cards that are 2 inch (5cm) Kewpies attached to a
    bisque holder:
        Reader
        Holding a Rose
        Mandolin Player
        Blunderboo
Place Card that is a Soldier shooting a bug
Place Cards that attach to a cup

Kewpie Doodle Dog

Alone in three sizes: 1½ inches (4cm), 3 inches (8cm),
    5 inches (13cm).
Attached to an olive green bisque box
With a sun flower
Molded to a bath tub

Jasperware objects
(Blue and white unless otherwise noted)

Bank
covered tall Bowl
flower Bowl
finger Bowl
sugar Bowl
Box ("Klothespin Box")
Clock (also in green and pink)
Hair receiver
Hatpin holder
Jar
Pitcher (also in green and pink)
wall Plaques (also in green and pink)
Plates
Sugar and cream set
various Vases

China (glazed bisque) objects

Bank
Kewpie lying on a Box with a lid
Child's tea set, includes:
    teapot, sugar and creamer, plates, saucers, cups
Child's Bavarian plate
Baby dishes and Baby feeding dishes
Creamers
Cups and saucers
Inkwell
various Perfume bottles
Pitcher
Planter (with the Thinker)
Plaques
talcum Powder shakers
salt and pepper Shakers
Tray (some have matching coasters)

ABOVE: Illustration 44. This 2 inch (5cm) *Action Kewpie* is holding a double gold wedding ring. This is the only example known of this figure. *Helen Sieverling Collection.*

RIGHT: Illustration 45. An Action Figure in a rare variant is *Kewpie* with a surprised look. Like most all-bisque figures, it is incised "O'NEILL." 3¼ inches tall (8cm). *Helen Sieverling Collection.*

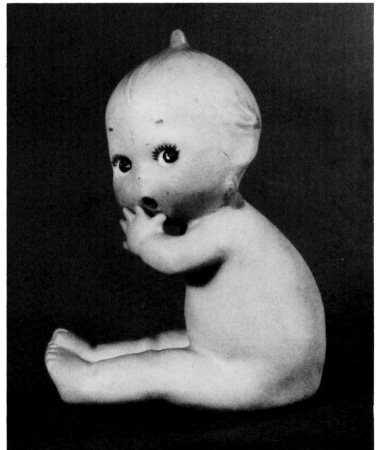

LEFT: Illustration 46. 2½ inch (6cm) *Governor* sitting in a wicker chair. This piece is not marked but it still carries the red heart sticker on the back and the round copyright sticker on the bottom. *Shirley Buchholz Collection.*

BELOW: Illustration 47. 4 inch (10cm) *Kewpie Policeman* from Germany. No markings. *Author's Collection.*

ABOVE: Illustration 48. Rare 2 inch (5cm) *Kewpie* with a peep (or chicken) coming out of an egg. The round copyright sticker is still attached to the back of the *Kewpie*. *Shirley Buchholz Collection.*

LEFT: Illustration 49. Rare 4½ inch (12cm) *Kewpie* vase. The birthday hat has a blue flower in it; the whistle in Kewpie's arms is bright pink. The vase portion of the figure is white. The base is incised "AKG 27." and is one of the few *Kewpie* items that carry the Kestner crown marking. *Shirley Buchholz Collection.*

RIGHT: Illustration 50. This *Kewpie* figurine is rare for two reasons: *Kewpie* is wearing a dress and is holding a cup that is decorated with gold trim. 5½ inches (14cm) tall. The back is incised "4541" with "Germany" in script. *Shirley Buchholz Collection.*

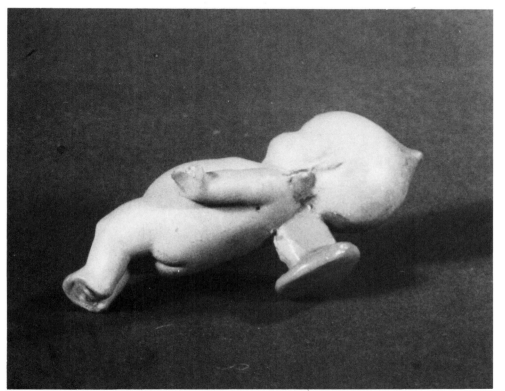

Illustration 51. 2¼ inch (6cm) *Kewpie* boutonniere meant to be inserted through a buttonhole. *Helen Sieverling Collection.*

Illustration 52. 2½ inch (6cm) *Kewpie* place card holder that attaches to a cup. *Shirley Buchholz Collection.*

Illustration 53. Place card holder showing the hooked opening for attachment to a cup and the slot for holding a place card. *Shirley Buchholz Collection.*

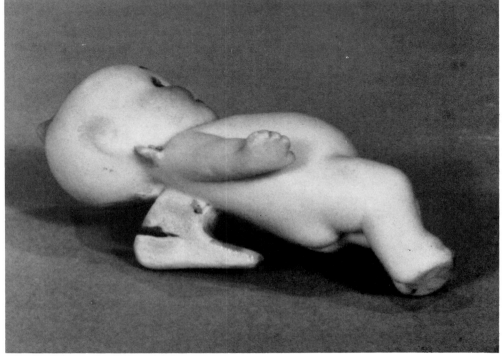

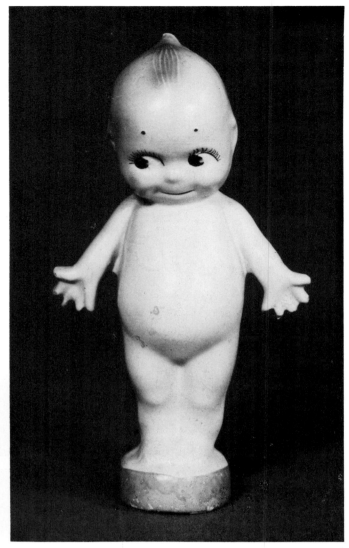

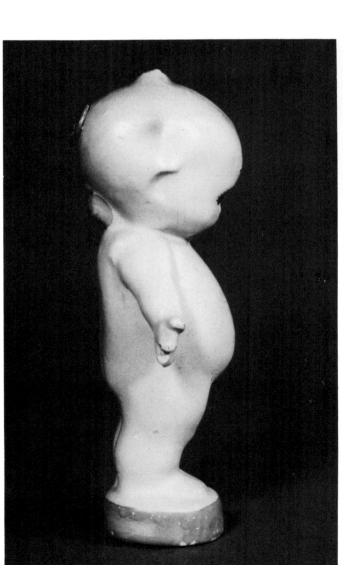

ABOVE: Illustration 54. All-composition *Kewpie* talcum container with painted features. 7 inches (18cm) tall. *Lillian Rohaly Collection.*

LEFT: Illustration 55. Side view of talcum powder holder. Note the bronze insert in the back of the head that is pierced with holes for shaking the talcum out. *Lillian Rohaly Collection.*

ABOVE: **Illustration 56.** Joseph L. Kallus drawing and plaster model of the Kewpie Huggers that were incorporated into the Jasper Ware plaques of 1973.

LEFT: **Illustration 57.** Joseph L. Kallus original for the plaques that he had copyrighted and produced in 1973. These plaques have a blue background with white decorations and they measure 7¼ inches (19cm) tall.

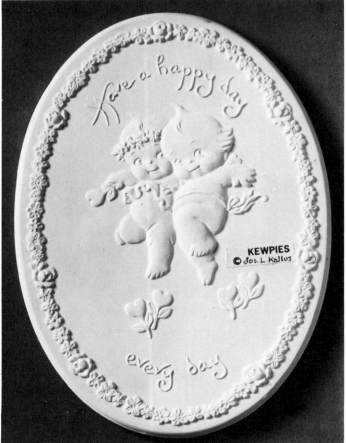

ABOVE: Illustration 58. The glass toothpick holder, at left has "SERIAL NO. 2862" molded to the bottom of the Kewpie part and "GEO BORGFELDT & CO., N.Y. / KEWPIE / REG. U.S. PAT OFF. / DES. PAT. 43680" molded to the open vase portion. The painted glass Christmas tree light is 3¼ inches (8cm) tall. *Lillian Rohaly Collection.*

RIGHT: Illustration 59. China salt and pepper set made in Germany. 2½ inches (6cm) tall. *Helen Sieverling Collection.*

ABOVE: Illustration 60. The Kewpie china dishes are a complete child's tea set. They are marked "COPYRIGHTED / ROSE O'NEILL WILSON / KEWPIE / GERMANY." *Helen Sieverling Collection.*

RIGHT: Illustration 61. *Dottie Darling and Kewpie*, incised only "JAPAN" is 3½ inches (9cm) tall. This is a variation of the *Kewpie Huggers. Helen Sieverling Collection.*

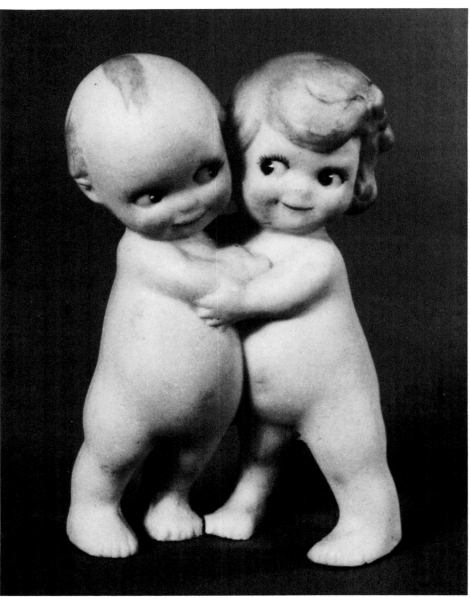

78

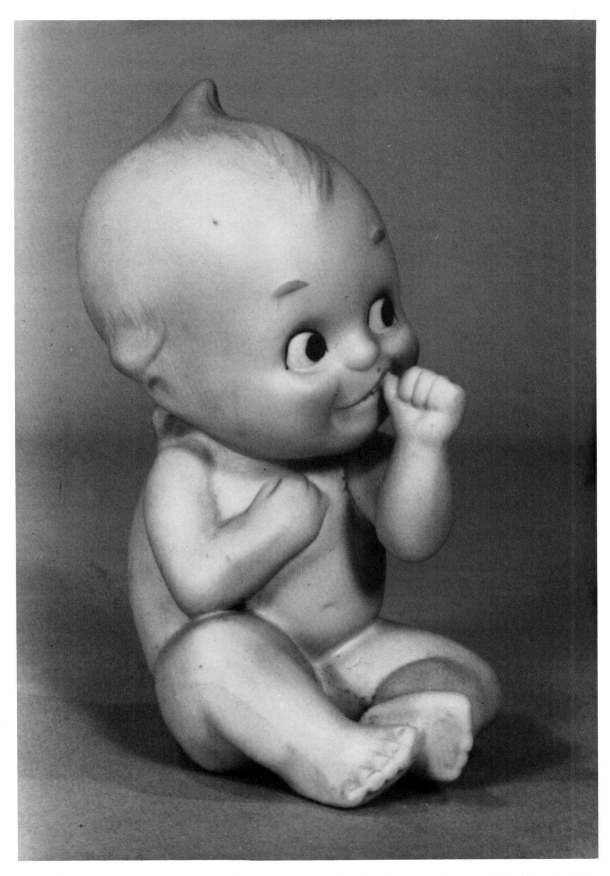

Illustration 62. *Kewpie* figurine by Lefton. Made in Japan, 1973. The *Thumb Sucker* is 4¾ inches (12cm) tall and is made from a smoothly finished bisque. *Author's Collection.*

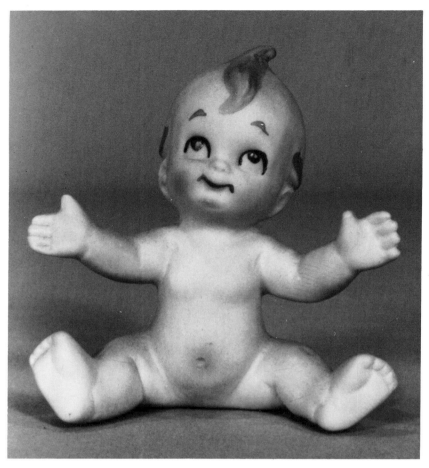

ABOVE: **Illustration 63.** 3½ inch (9cm) *Kewpie* by Lefton, Made in Japan, 1973. *Author's Collection.*

RIGHT: **Illustration 64.** 3¼ inch (8cm) *Kewpie* by Lefton of Japan, 1973. *Bette Ann Axe Collection.*

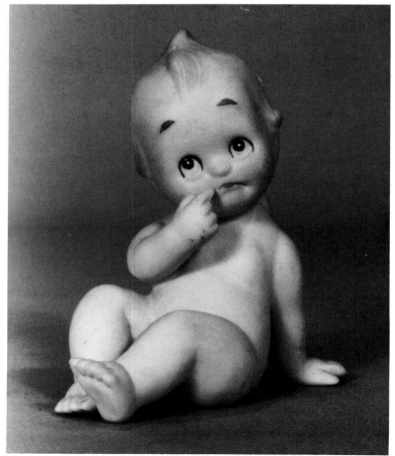

All-composition *Scootles* that is a rare original combination of a different *Scootles* head and a *Kewpie* body. This doll was a sample from Joseph L. Kallus. *Helen Sieverling Collection.*

12 inch (31cm) all-composition *Scootles, 1930s. Lillian Rohaly Collection.*

12½ inch (32cm) all-composition black
Scootles, a rare version of this doll,
Effanbee, circa 1949. *Helen Sieverling
Collection.*

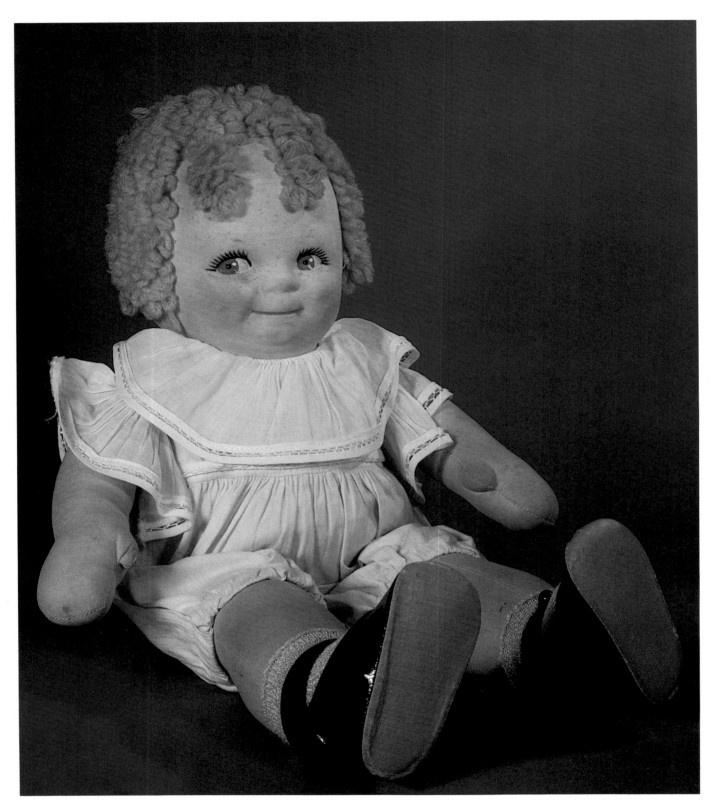

18½ inch (47cm) all-cloth *Scootles* with painted eyes and a yarn wig. *Helen Sieverling Collection.*

16 inch (41cm) vinyl *Scootles*, 1960s-1970s, with sleep eyes and molded hair.

Baby Bundie, Joseph L. Kallus' first doll. She is 12 inches (31cm) tall with jointed arms only. *Helen Sieverling Collection.*

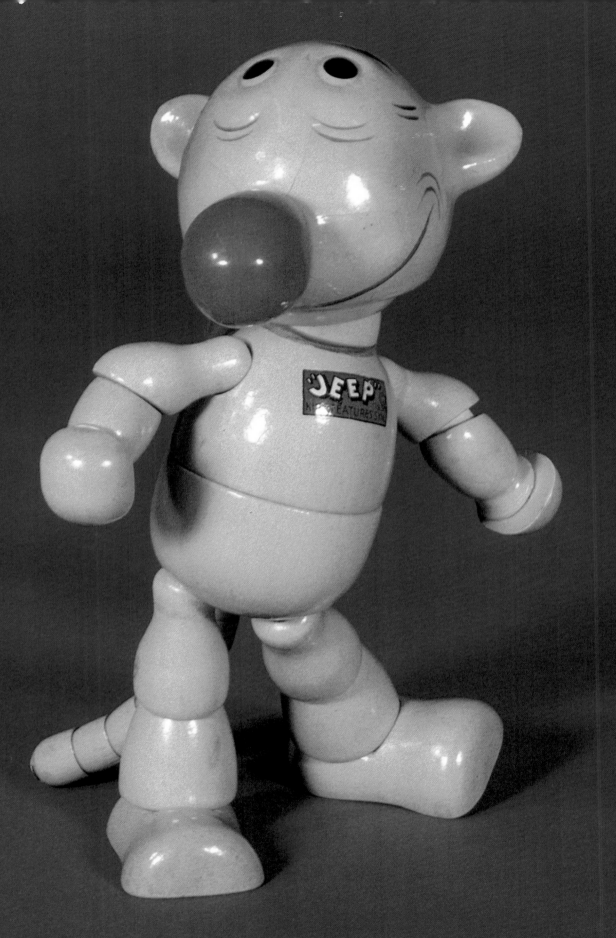

9 inch (23cm) *Jeep*, 1940s. All-composition with wooden segments for the tail and arms and legs.

17 inch (43cm) *Margie*, 1958. All-vinyl and fully-jointed with rooted hair and sleep eyes.

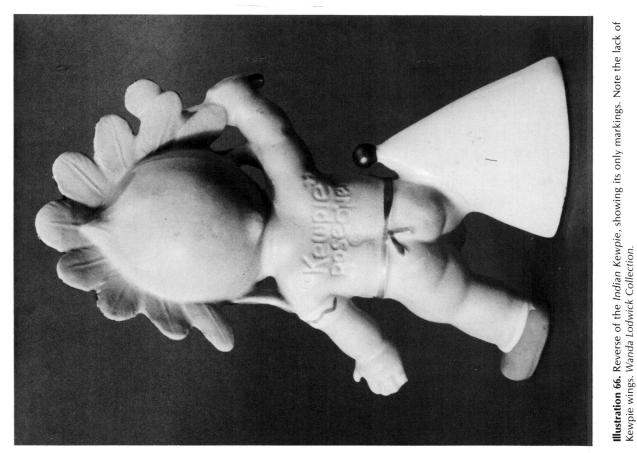

Illustration 65. Although this *Action Kewpie* is of a later date — 1960s or 1970s, it is quite rare and different. It is 4 inches (10cm) tall. *Wanda Lodwick Collection.*

Illustration 66. Reverse of the *Indian Kewpie*, showing its only markings. Note the lack of Kewpie wings. *Wanda Lodwick Collection.*

ABOVE: **Illustration 67.** 5 inch (13cm) *Kewpie-type* figurine, probably from Japan in the 1970s. Blue wings on back. *Shirley Buchholz Collection.*

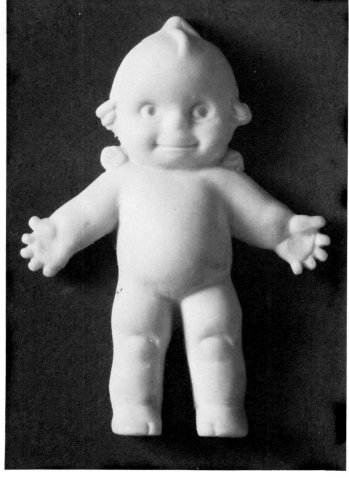

Illustration 68. A model for Kewpie soap by Joseph Kallus.

Illustration 69. Joseph Kallus models for Kewpie jewelry.

Illustration 70. 2½ inch (6cm) copy of the *Kewpie Doodle Dog*, a current product made in Japan by Shackman. The finish is glazed china. *Author's Collection.*

Illustration 71. 3½ inch (9cm) *Kewpie bisque figurines made in Korea by Extra Special, Inc., 1985, under license from Jesco, Inc. These figurines are beautifully sculpted and finished and well-painted in muted colors. Extra Special, Inc., did not stay in business long so these figurines are quite scarce. Bette Ann Axe Collection.*

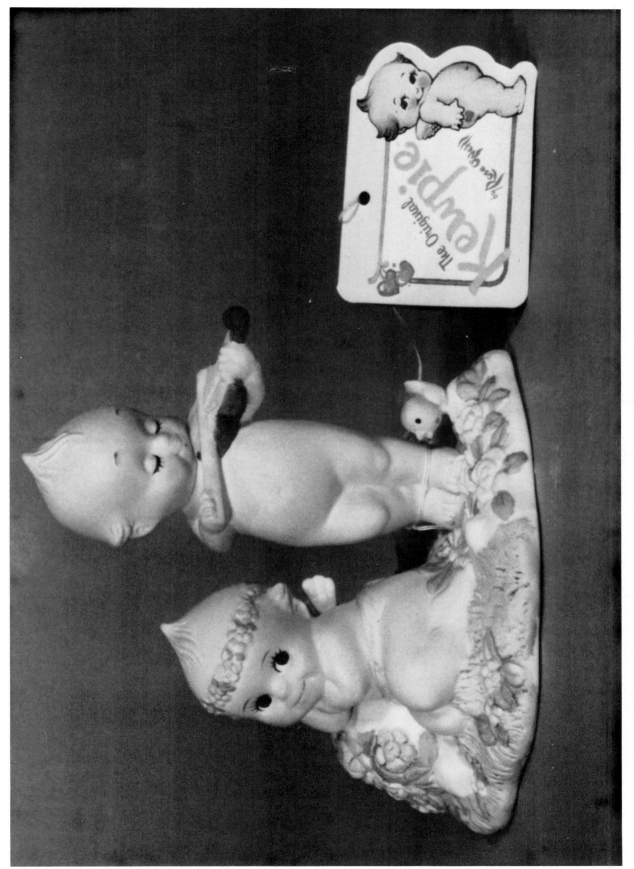

Illustration 72. 4 inch (10cm) *Sweet Serenade*, Item No. 5160 from Extra Special, Inc., 1985, under license to Jesco, Inc. Made in Korea and stamped with the Kewpie logo, citing Rose O'Neill as the creator of the Kewpie. *Author's Collection.*

LEFT: Illustration 73. This "Kewpie" item is probably a rip-off and was not a licensed product. It is a shiny papier-mâché coin bank that was made in Hong Kong. Incised on the back: "©1977 A. BEE SYNDICATE, INC." *Author's Collection.*

BELOW: Illustration 74. All-bisque heads that were a souvenir for a doll convention, March 1980. The head measures 5 inches (13cm); the completed doll is 10 inches (25cm) tall. *Lillian Rohaly Collection.*

PART III

THE DOLLS OF ROSE O'NEILL AND JOSEPH L. KALLUS

ROSE O'NEILL DOLLS

The most famous doll associated with Rose O'Neill will always be *Kewpie*. Kewpie originated as illustrations for magazines and Joseph L. Kallus translated the O'Neill drawings into three-dimensional forms, including figurines and dolls. The first dolls were made in Germany in 1912 of all-bisque with jointed arms only. These dolls were made in many different sizes from 2 inch (5cm) to about 13 inch (33cm) and so many were produced in the early years that the molds would have been used over and over, creating all of the size variations found in these dolls. The most common sizes are given in the charts on pages 98 and 99.

In 1925 Rose O'Neill created *Scootles*. She may have done the original sculpting, but Kallus changed and refined the design over the years. In late 1940 Rose O'Neill created *Ho-Ho*, the Little Laughing Buddha, which was more of a figurine than a doll, as it had no moving parts, and Kallus later refined and changed this when he marketed *Ho-Ho*, especially in vinyl in the 1960s.

Mr. Kallus created a great many dolls and toys from his own designs and those of others. His greatest period of production was during the 1920s, 1930s and 1940s. The first doll that Kallus obtained his own design copyright for was *Baby Bundie* in 1918. He continued to create new baby dolls over the years, the last of his original designs being *Miss Peep* in vinyl in the 1960s. He also did many dolls and figures for advertising firms, such as *Mr. Peanut* and the *RCA Radiotron* doll. Using a design that originated as a drawing or a cartoon strip, he did various characters such as *Felix the Cat, Bonzo* and *Little Annie Rooney*. From animated cartoons he rendered the creations *Betty Boop* and *Pinocchio* in doll form.

The most original concept in doll design that Kallus invented is one that uses a composition or wooden head with body portions, arms and legs that are wooden

Illustration 75. Standing all-bisque *Kewpie* dolls with jointed arms. The bottom of the feet on these dolls is usually incised "O'NEILL." The heart sticker on the chest says "KEWPIE;" an additional sticker carries the 1913 copyright. The sizes shown here are 2¼ inches (6cm), 5 inches (13cm), 6 inches (15cm), 8⅝ inches (22cm), 8¾ inches (22cm), and 12 inches (31cm). Note that the painted eyes glance to either side, depending on the *Kewpie. Helen Sieverling Collection.*

segments strung together with elastic. This gives the figures more flexibility in posing them and adds more play value for children. Notable among these dolls are *Joy, Margie, Pinkie, Howdy Doody* and *Superman,* all of which have remained in rather good condition for 40 or 50 years because of the sturdy wooden construction.

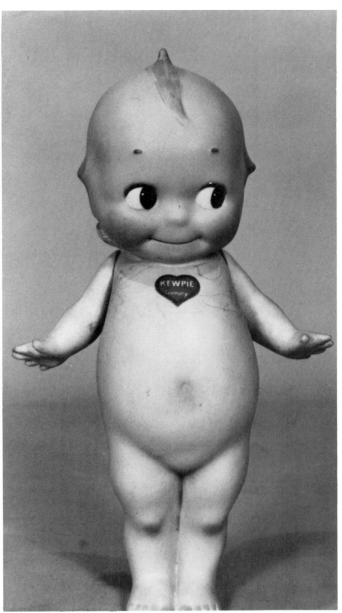

Illustration 76. 9 inch (23cm) all-bisque *Kewpie* doll with jointed arms. *Author's Collection.*

Illustration 77. Close-up of the all-bisque *Kewpie* doll with jointed arms. The delicately feathered painted eyelashes do not show properly because of the angle of *Kewpie's* head, *Author's Collection.*

KEWPIE

All-bisque

1912+

Made in Germany by Kestner, Gebr. Voight, Herman Voight and others. Made in U.S.A. by Fulper Pottery.

1. With jointed arms only.

    Sizes:

2 inches (5cm)		7½ inches (19cm)
2½ inches (6cm)		8 inches (20cm)
4 inches (10cm)		9 inches (23cm)
4½ inches (12cm)		10½ inches (27cm)
5 inches (13cm)		11 inches (28cm)
6 inches (15cm)		12 inches (31cm)
7 inches (18cm)		13 inches (33cm)

2. All-bisque with jointed arms and legs.

    Sizes:

4 inches (10cm)
5½ inches (14cm)

3. Bisque shoulder head; arm; legs. Cloth body. Painted eyes.

    Sizes:

6 inches (15cm)
12 inches (31cm)

4. Bisque head; flange neck; cloth body or composition body; round glass eyes.

    13½ inches (34cm)

Celluloid

1915+

Made in Germany by Karl Standfuss. Made in Japan by various firms.

Most have jointed arms.

Sizes:

2 inches (5cm)	5¼ inches (13cm)
2¼ inches (6cm)	6½ inches (17cm)
2½ inches (6cm)	7 inches (18cm)
3 inches (8cm)	7½ inches (19cm)
3¼ inches (8cm)	8 inches (20cm)
3½ inches (9cm)	10 inches (25cm)
4 inches (10cm)	11¼ inches (29cm)
4½ inches (12cm)	22 inches (56cm)
5 inches (13cm)	

The 2¼ inch - 2½ inch (6-7cm) size also comes in a black version, referred to as a *Hottentot*.

Celluloid continued

There are also many novelty *Kewpies* in celluloid with no jointed parts:

3 inches	(8cm)	with a rabbit
3 inches	(8cm)	*Instructor*
3 inches	(8cm)	and other sizes, Bride and Groom for a wedding cake decoration
3½ inches	(9cm)	*Huggers*
5 inches	(13cm)	with a painted bathing suit and hat

Jointed arms two-in-one doll:

2½ inches	(6cm)	*Kewpie* on one side; *Billikin* on the other
4 inches	(10cm)	*Kewpie* on one side; *Billikin* on the other

---

Composition

1916+

Made in U.S.A. by Joseph L. Kallus for Rex Doll Co., Mutual Doll Co., Cameo Doll Co., Noma Electric Corporation (Effanbee), and Effanbee Doll Corporation.

1. With jointed arms; usually attached to a base or "pedestal;" can have mohair wigs over molded *Kewpie* hair. (early years)

    Sizes:

7 inches (18cm)		11½ inches (29cm)
8 inches (20cm)		12 inches (31cm)
10 inches (25cm)		

2. With jointed arms; free-standing with legs apart; also as black dolls (1940s)

    11½ inches (29cm)

3. Fully-jointed (1940s)

    Sizes:

8 inches (20cm)		13 inches (33cm)
11 inches (28cm)		15 inches (38cm)
12 inches (31cm)		

4. Composition head; cloth body

    Sizes:

12 inches (31cm)
23 inches (58cm)

Note: In 1923 an all-composition *Kewpie* sold for 58¢ for the 8 inch (20cm) size; in the late 1940s the fully-jointed composition *Kewpie* from Noma (Effanbee) was $2.00.

All-Cloth

1926+

Made in U.S.A. after 1926 by King Innovations, Inc. Made in U.S.A. after 1936 by Richard G. Kreuger, Inc.

Sizes for the Richard G. Kreuger, Inc.*Kewpies*, made of all-cloth with a mask face and a jersey body in red, blue, green, coral, yellow or pink:

8	inches	(20cm)
11	inches	(28cm)
14	inches	(36cm)
17	inches	(43cm)
21	inches	(53cm)

Sizes for the King Innovations *Kewpies*, made with a mask face and a plush body:

9	inches	(23cm)
12	inches	(31cm)
15	inches	(38cm)
18	inches	(46cm)
22	inches	(56cm)

Sizes for King Innovations *Kewpies* in all-cloth wearing dresses:

11	inches	(28cm)

Hard Plastic

1949

Effanbee Doll Company, Inc.

From 1946 to 1953 the Effanbee Doll Company was owned by the Noma Electric Corporation. Noma-Effanbee made all-composition dolls from 1946 to 1949. The hard plastic *Kewpie* dolls made in 1949 may be the very first all-hard plastic dolls packaged in an Effanbee box, although they still carried the Cameo label. The Effanbee hard plastic *Kewpie* has sleep eyes and is fully-jointed. From 1950 to 1953 Noma-Effanbee continued to make hard plastic and vinyl dolls. After 1953 the Effanbee Doll Company, Inc., was under the ownership of Bernard Baum (the son of Hugo Baum, who with Bernard L. Fleischaker founded Effanbee in 1910), Perry Epstein and Morris Lutz. In 1971 Effanbee was purchased by Leroy Fadem and Roy R. Raizen. As of this writing (1986) Effanbee has been sold again.

The all-hard plastic, fully-jointed *Kewpie* with sleep eyes from Effanbee is 13½ inches tall (34cm).

In 1986 Jesco, Inc., made a 6 inch (15cm) hard-plastic *Kewpie* that has jointed arms.

Vinyl

1952+

Cameo Doll Products; Strombecker Corp. 1969-1973; Milton Bradley (Amsco), 1973-1976; Knickerbocker, 1972; Jesco, Inc., 1982+.

All the vinyl dolls carried a label citing Cameo Doll Products, although they were distributed and/or made by other companies. The vinyl dolls are marked "CAMEO // ©." Some also have the initials "J.L.K." A few have heads marked "1965 J.L.K."

Sizes of vinyl dolls:

1. With inset plastic eyes:

 9½ inches (24cm)

2. Vinyl head and arms; blow mold body and legs (thin plastic):

 13½ inches (34cm)
 19½ inches (50cm)

3. With rooted hair:

 13 inches (33cm)
 21 inches (53cm)

4. *Thinker.* (One piece):

 4 inches (10cm)

5. *Ragsy.* Jointed head; one-piece body:

 8 inches (20cm)

6. All-vinyl. Jointed head only:

 4¼ inches (11cm)
 6 inches (15cm)
 11 inches (28cm)

7. All-vinyl. Fully-jointed:

8	inches	(20cm)	16	inches	(41cm)
12	inches	(31cm)	27	inches	(69cm)
14	inches	(36cm)			

8. *Kewpie Gal.* Has molded hair with an inset cloth ribbon:

 8½ inches (22cm)
 12 inches (31cm)

9. *Kuddly Kewpie.* Bodies are a combination of plush and cloth; some have bunny ears.

 7 inches (18cm) in seated position
 9 inches (23cm) in seated position

10. Jesco *Kewpies* in all-vinyl:

 12 inches (31cm)
 18 inches (46cm)
 26½ inches (67cm)

Illustration 78. 6 inch (15cm) all-bisque *Kewpie* with jointed arms and legs. These *Kewpies* with the extra joints are much rarer than those with only jointed arms. *Helen Sieverling Collection.*

BELOW: Illustration 79. Bisque shoulder head doll on a cloth body; the hands and feet are also bisque. The head is marked: "9268." The shoulder head at the right is 2½ inches tall (6cm) and is marked: "9268/3" on the back. The bisque shoulder head dolls are even rarer than the all-bisque ones that are fully-jointed. *Helen Sieverling Collection.*

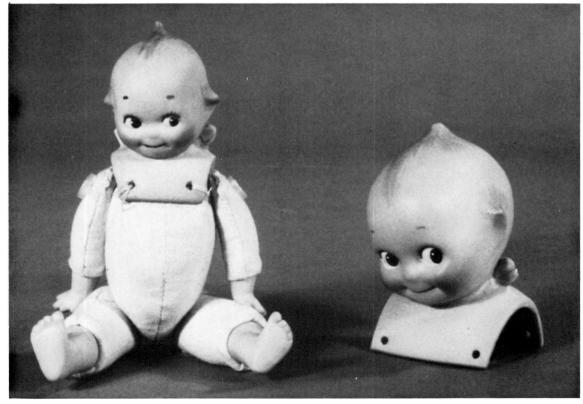

Illustration 80. *Kewpie* bride and groom; celluloid with jointed arms; 3¼ inches tall (8cm). Made in Germany. Note the carefully painted eyelashes. *Author's Collection.*

Illustration 81. 2¼ inch (6cm) black celluloid *Kewpies*, called *Hottentots*, with jointed arms. Made in Germany. *Author's Collection.*

OPPOSITE PAGE: **Illustration 82.** All-celluloid *Kewpies* with jointed arms, from left to right: 14½ inch (37cm) made in Japan; 9 inch (23cm) black version with no topknot; 8½ inch (22cm) made in Germany. *Helen Sieverling Collection.*

Illustration 83. Black *Kewpies* with jointed arms in two versions. At left: All-bisque in a chocolate color with blue painted wings; marked "O'NEILL" on bottom; 4½ inches (12cm) tall. At right: 7 inch (18cm) black celluloid with wings, Made in Japan. *Lillian Rohaly Collection.*

LEFT: **Illustration 84.** All-celluloid *Kewpies,* probably made in Japan. The one at the top is fully-jointed and is 2 inches (5cm) tall. The two at the bottom, enclosed in the ribbon, are only 1 inch (3cm) tall and they are stick pins with no moving parts. *Helen Sieverling Collection.*

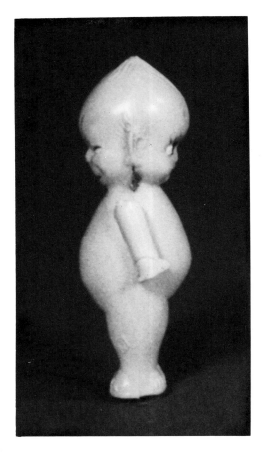

CLOCKWISE: Illustration 85. A rare 2½ inch (6cm) *Kewpie-Billikin* combination of celluloid with no markings. The Kewpie portion (shown at the right here) has green painted Kewpie wings. *Lillian Rohaly Collection.*

Illustration 86. The Kewpie side of Lillian Rohaly's *Kewpie-Billikin* novelty figure.

Illustration 87. The Billikin side of Lillian Rohaly's *Kewpie-Billikin*. Note that the jointed arms serve both sides of the figure.

Illustration 88. This 4¼ inch (11cm) figure is one of the most unusual of all Kewpie-inspired items from Japan. It is a *Kewpie* holding a *Kewpie* holding a *Kewpie*. This shows the largest figure of the three-piece group from the front. *Lillian Rohaly Collection.*

Illustration 89. Back view of *Kewpie* holding a *Kewpie* holding a *Kewpie* from Japan in all-celluloid. *Lillian Rohaly Collection.*

Illustration 90. In the center is a large papier-mâché *Kewpie* that was used as an advertising piece. It is 33 inches (84cm) tall. The front of the base is incised: "KEWPIE TWINS / REG. U.S. PAT OFF. / SHOES FOR CHILDREN." A label inside reads: "OLD KING COLE INC. / CANTON, OHIO." The little composition figure at the left is 7 inches (18cm) and the doll at the right is 12½ inches tall (32cm). The two smaller figures are attached to a blue pedestal; they are all-composition with jointed arms. All of these *Kewpies* probably date from before 1920. *Helen Sieverling Collection.*

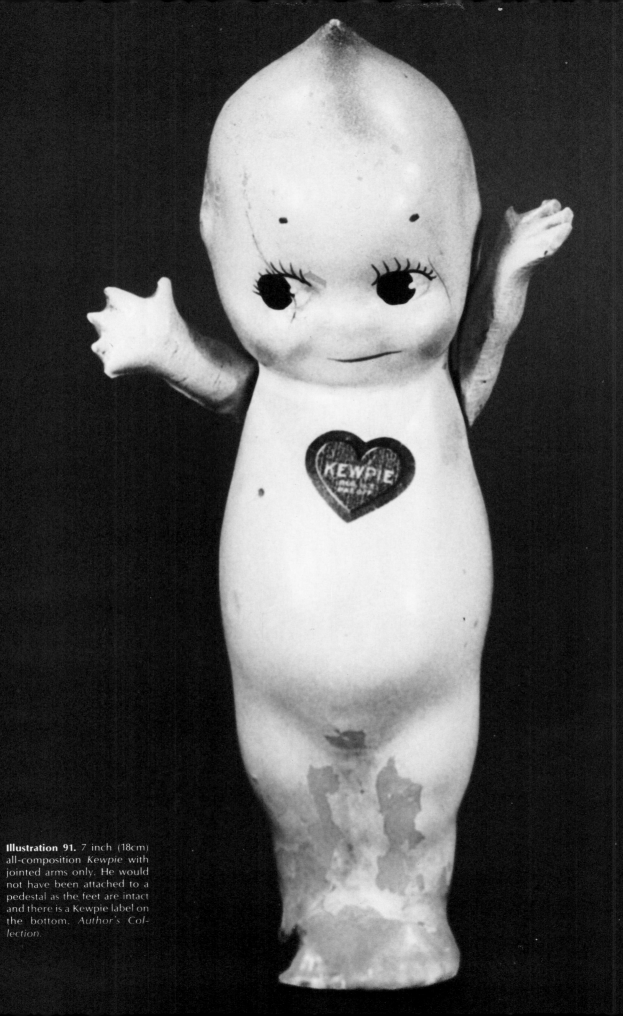

Illustration 91. 7 inch (18cm) all-composition *Kewpie* with jointed arms only. He would not have been attached to a pedestal as the feet are intact and there is a Kewpie label on the bottom. *Author's Collection.*

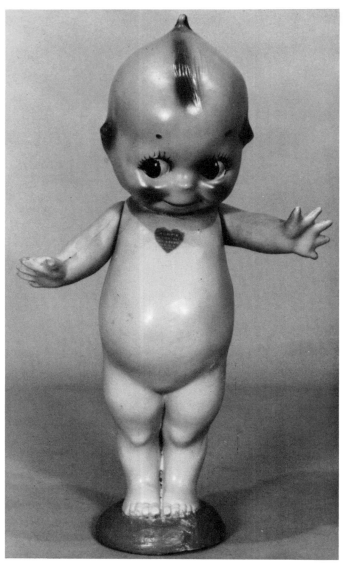

Illustration 92. 12 inch (31cm) early composition "carnival" *Kewpie* with feet molded to a pedestal. Only the arms are jointed. This lightweight composition *Kewpie* has remained in good condition with bright coloring, which is rarely seen on the older dolls that were originally carnival prizes. *Author's Collection.*

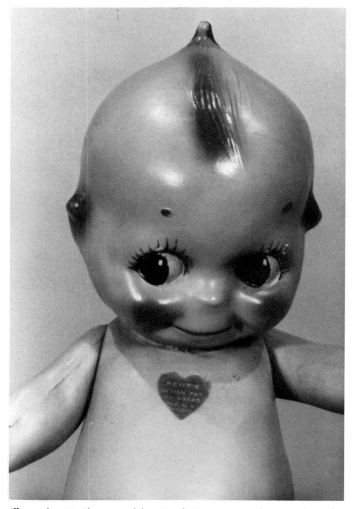

Illustration 93. Close-up of the 12 inch (31cm) carnival *Kewpie* from the early 20th century. *Author's Collection.*

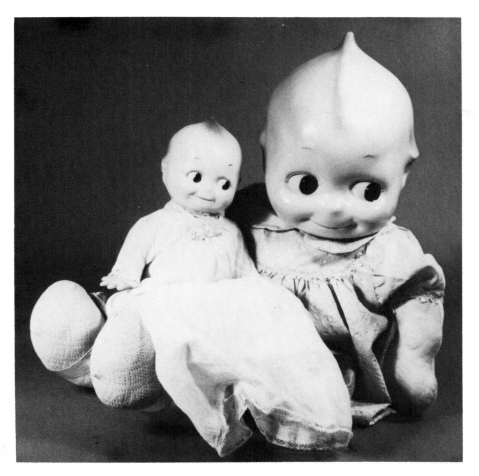

Illustration 94. Two *Kewpie* babies with composition heads and cloth bodies. The sizes are 12 inches (31cm) and 23 inches (58cm). The smaller one also has composition lower arms. Neither doll is marked and they probably date from before the 1940s. *Helen Sieverling Collection.*

Illustration 95. Noma Electric toy catalog, late 1940s showing the two styles of all-composition *Kewpies* from that time. The fully-jointed version at the left does not have the heart label on the chest, as the one at the right with jointed arms only does. The dressed *Kewpie* is 13 inches (33cm) tall; the undressed sample is 11½ inches (29cm).

Kewpie doll

DESIGN AND COPYRIGHT *by Rose O'Neill*

No. 9713—DRESSED KEWPIE DOLL
The most famous doll in the world — designed by Rose O'Neill. Known and loved by children everywhere. Dressed in colorful rompers, knitted socks and laced booties. Fully jointed—assumes many lovable poses—she sits, she walks, she kicks—she tilts her head. SHE'S A HONEY! Sturdily constructed, realistically colored and hand painted features. Stands 13" high. Packed in beautiful display box. 2 dozen to shipping carton. Weight 45 lbs.
F.O.B. Holyoke, Mass.; Port Allegany, Pa.; Milford, Del.; New York, N. Y.

A CAMEO PRODUCT

No. 9703—KEWPIE DOLL
A famous name doll — designed by Rose O'Neill. Tops in personality and popular in price. Strongly constructed to take knocks and come up smiling. Impish eyes—jointed arms — delights children. Stands 11½" high. Individually boxed. 3 dozen to shipping carton. Weight 37 lbs.
F.O.B. New York, N. Y.

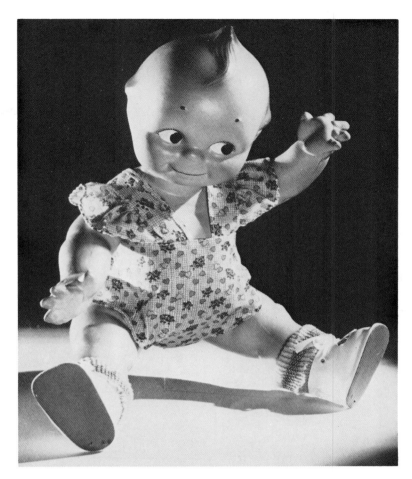

OPPOSITE PAGE: Illustration 96. A 13 inch (33cm) fully-jointed Noma Electric (Effanbee) *Kewpie* in a sunsuit, late 1940s.

Illustration 97. Another Noma all-composition *Kewpie* in a different patterned sunsuit. All-fully jointed composition *Kewpies* should be dressed this way, imitating their original presentation.

Illustration 98. Two fully-jointed *Kewpies*. Their sizes are 13 inches (33cm) and 15 inches (38cm). *Helen Sieverling Collection.*

111

Illustration 99. Back cover of *Junior Home for Parent and Child*, November 1932, showing all-cloth *Kewpies* by King Innovations, Inc. At the bottom of the page is a line of Winnie the Pooh characters also by King. *Author's Collection.*

Illustration 100. 8 inch (20cm) all-cloth *Kewpie* by King Innovations, Inc., shown with the original box. The jersey body is green. *Helen Sieverling Collection.*

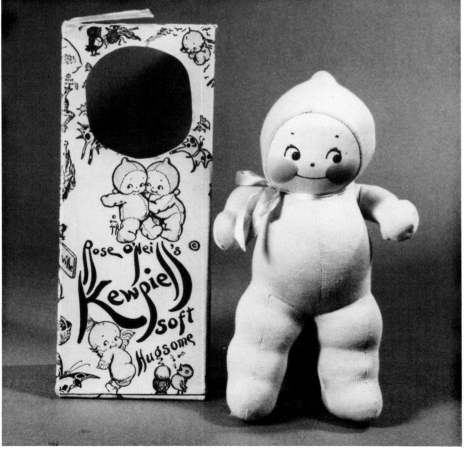

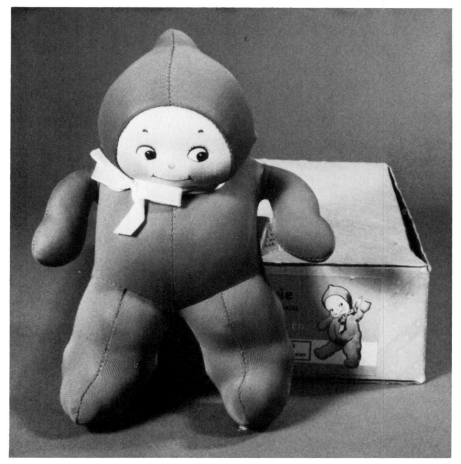

CLOCKWISE: Illustration 101. 12 inch (31cm) all-cloth *Kewpie* from King Innovations, Inc., with bunny ears on the head. The jersey body is pink. *Helen Sieverling Collection.*

Illustration 102. 21 inch (53cm) all-cloth *Kewpie* by King Innovations, Inc. The dress is labeled "KEWPIE COPYRIGHT ROSE O'NEILL," but it is not known if it is original to the doll. *Helen Sieverling Collection.*

Illustration 103. 8 inch (20cm) all-cloth *Kewpie* by Richard G. Kreuger, Inc., 1930s. The jersey body is red; the box is original to the doll. Note that there is no apparent difference between the King Innovations *Kewpies* and those with a Kreuger label. *Helen Sieverling Collection.*

Illustration 104. 13½ inch (34cm) all-hard plastic, fully-jointed *Kewpie* with sleep eyes from Effanbee. Illustration from the 1949 Effanbee doll catalog.

Illustration 105. Back cover of the 1949 Effanbee doll catalog.

Illustration 106. 9 inch (23cm) all-hard plastic *Kewpie* with jointed arms. Back incised: "KEWPIE / ©BY ROSE O'NEILL." Probably dates from the 1950s. *Author's Collection.*

BELOW: Illustration 107. 6 inch (15cm) all-hard plastic *Kewpie* by Jesco with jointed arms, 1986. This doll is part of a "Kewpie Kard" that is a display box with a front that includes original artwork with a verse by Rose O'Neill.

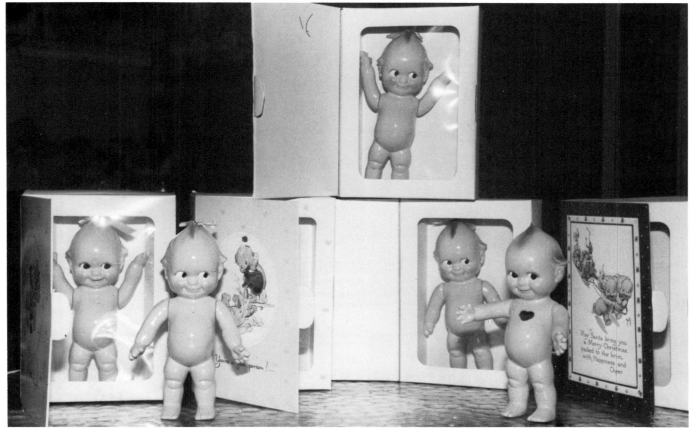

Illustration 108. Hang tag for Cameo dolls. The drawing is of Joseph L. Kallus' daughter when she was two years old.

BELOW: Illustration 109. Samples of Joseph L. Kallus' vinyl *Kewpies*. The sizes range from 4 inches (10cm) to 27 inches (69cm). The vinyl *Kewpies* were very popular and widely distributed in the 1960s and the 1970s, although they were first produced in about 1952.

Illustration 111. 9½ inch (24cm) all-vinyl *Kewpie Twins* by Cameo. The glassine eyes are stationary; only the heads are jointed.

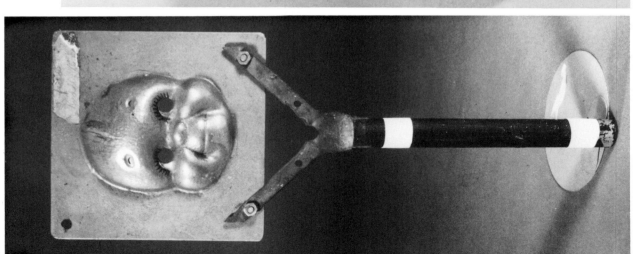

Illustration 110. Aluminum face mask for spray painting the eyes of a vinyl Kewpie.

117

ABOVE and OPPOSITE PAGE: Illustrations 112, 113 and **114.** *Kewpie Twins* with glassine eyes in various costumes.

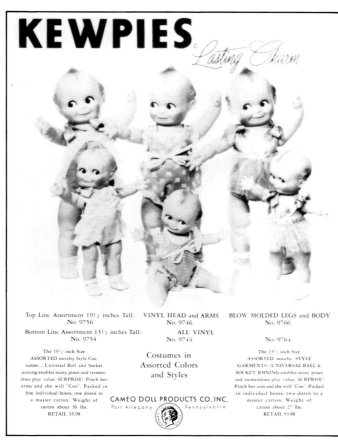

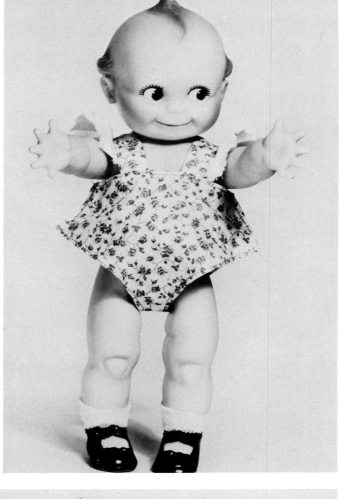

Illustration 116. Advertising for Cameo *Kewpies*.

KEWPIES *Lasting Charm*

| Top Line Assortment 19½ inches Tall: No. 9756 | VINYL HEAD and ARMS No. 9746 | BLOW MOLDED LEGS and BODY No. 9766 |
| Bottom Line Assortment 13½ inches Tall: No. 9754 | ALL VINYL No. 9744 | No. 9764 |

The 19½ inch Size ASSORTED novelty Style Costumes...Universal Ball and Socket joining enables many poses and tremendous play value. SURPRISE! Pinch her arms and she will "Coo". Packed in fine individual boxes, one dozen to a master carton. Weight of carton about 30 lbs.
RETAIL $5.98

Costumes in Assorted Colors and Styles

CAMEO DOLL PRODUCTS CO., INC.
Port Allegany   Pennsylvania

The 13½ inch Size ASSORTED novelty STYLE GARMENTS—UNIVERSAL BALL & SOCKET JOINING enables many poses and tremendous play value. SURPRISE! Pinch her arm and she will "Coo". Packed in individual boxes, two dozen to a master carton. Weight of carton about 27 lbs.
RETAIL $3.98

TOP RIGHT and RIGHT: Illustrations 117 and 118. *Kewpies* with thin plastic bodies and legs. The remainder of the doll is vinyl. This construction and design gave *Kewpie* a rather awkward look, as the legs seem too long.

Illustration 119. Floppy *Kewpie* with a cloth body in sizes of 17 inches (43cm) and 21 inches (53cm). It is not known if these dolls were produced.

Illustration 120. The vinyl *Kewpie* at the right has rooted hair. Although some of the early composition *Kewpies* had a mohair wig over molded hair, this effect did not translate well in a vinyl doll design. *Kewpie* always looks better with wispy, painted hair!

Illustrations 123 and 124. Various Cameo *Kewpies* in their original outfits. These dolls were distributed by Cameo, Milton Bradley (Amsco) and Strombecker.

Illustrations 125 and 126. Various Cameo *Kewpies* in their original outfits. These dolls were distributed by Cameo, Milton Bradley (Amsco) and Strombecker.

Illustrations 127 to 129. Various Cameo *Kewpies* in their original outfits. These dolls were distributed by Cameo, Milton Bradley (Amsco) and Strombecker.

Illustrations 130 and 131. Various Cameo *Kewpies* in their original outfits. These dolls were distributed by Cameo, Milton Bradley (Amsco) and Strombecker.

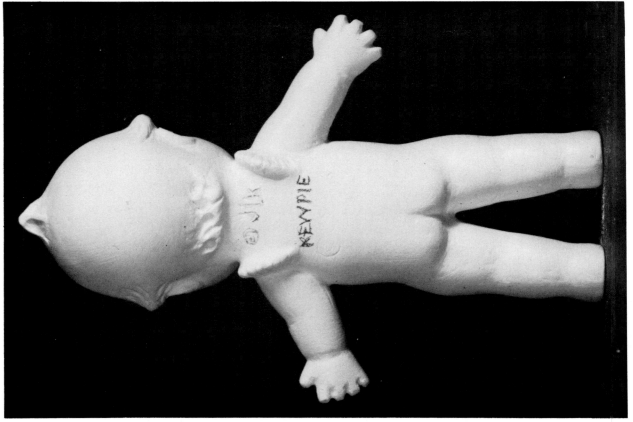

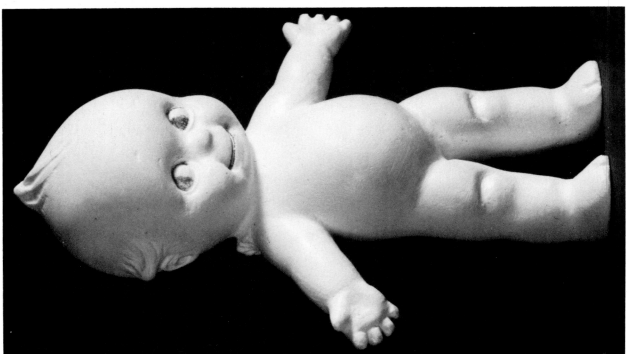

Illustrations 132 and **133.** Plaster model for Joseph Kallus' vinyl *Kewpie*. This sample does not have a jointed head, which would be changed for the vinyl dolls.

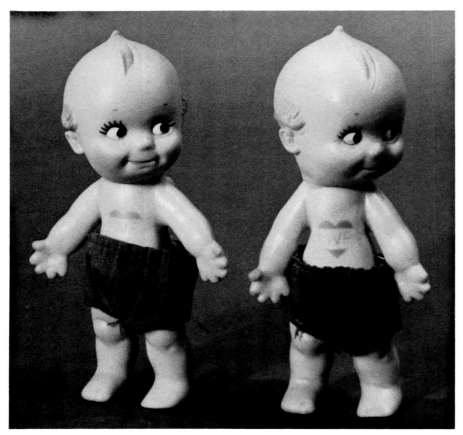

Illustration 134. 4¼ inch (11cm) all-vinyl *Kewpies* with jointed heads. *Author's Collection.*

OPPOSITE PAGE: Illustration 136. Jointed head *Kewpie* in still another version of the sunsuit.

RIGHT: Illustration 135. 11 inch (28cm) *Kewpie Sleeper* with a jointed head.

Illustration 122. *Kewpie* with curly rooted hair, which has a better appearance than the straight hair does.

Illustration 137. The vinyl version of *Kewpie* on the left has a jointed head; the one at the right is fully-jointed and her shoes are prototypes, as the shoes on the vinyl dolls were not made of cloth and they did not have heels on them.

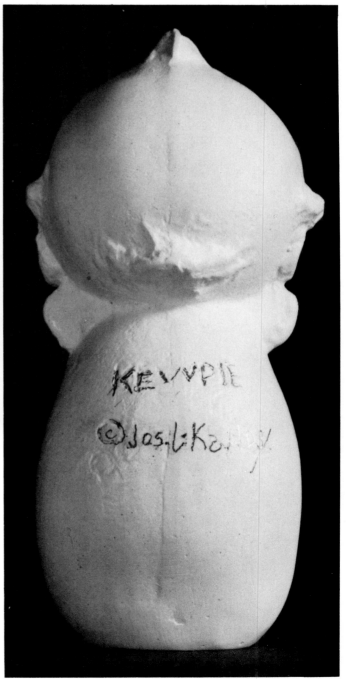

Illustration 138 and **139.** Plaster model for *Kewpie Thinker* that was executed in vinyl in a 4 inch (10cm) size.

Illustration 140. All-vinyl *Kewpie Thinker*. Compare this figure with the all-bisque *Kewpie Thinker* from the early years of *Kewpie* production (**Illustration 42**). *Author's Collection.*

BELOW: Illustration 141. Plaster models for Joseph Kallus' vinyl version of the *Thinker*. Note that the third figure from the left has inset glass or plastic eyes.

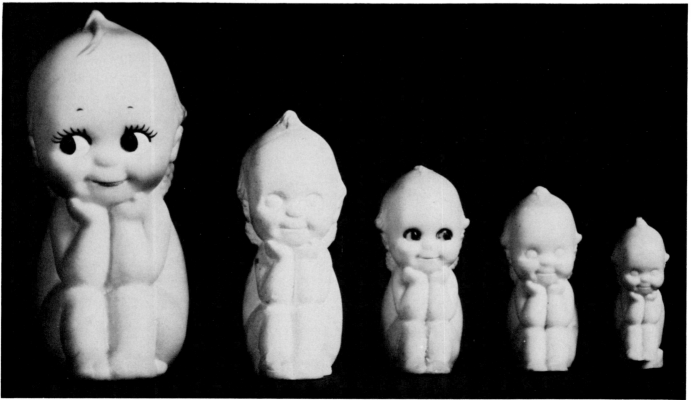

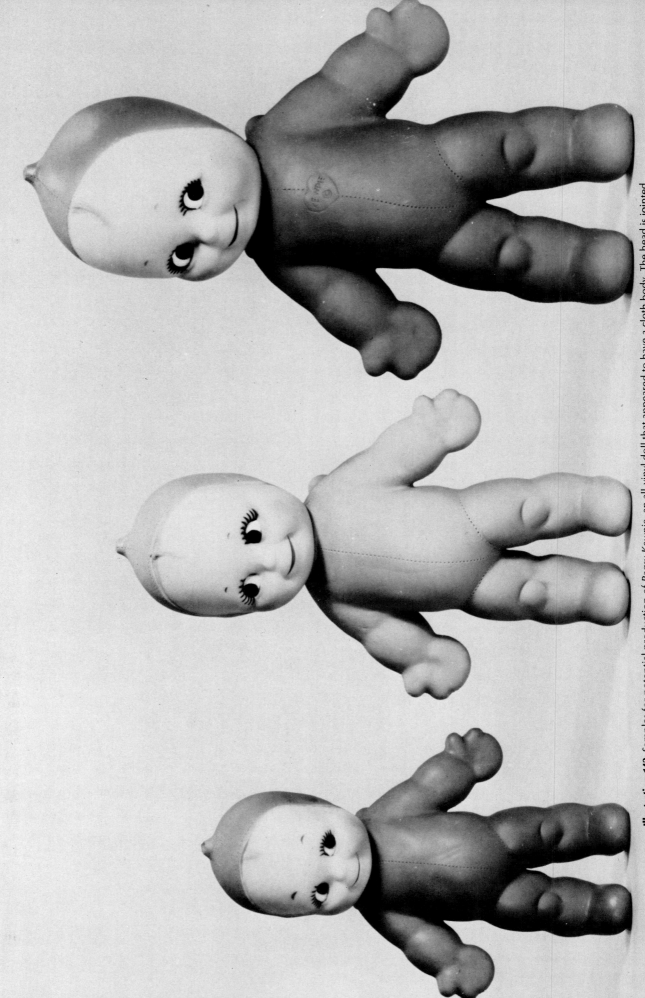

Illustration 142. Samples for potential production of *Ragsy Kewpie*, an all-vinyl doll that appeared to have a cloth body. The head is jointed.

Illustration 143. *Ragsy Kewpie* wearing a sunsuit. This photograph is from Joseph Kallus' files; the finished doll was not sold in this costume.

ABOVE: Illustration 144. Model for *Ragsy Kewpie* that has jointed arms and legs. This sample was not put into production.

Illustration 145. 7 inch (18cm) *Kuddle Kewpie* with a vinyl face that has inset plastic eyes; plush body. *Helen Sieverling Collection.*

Illustration 146. *Kuddle Kewpie* with a vinyl face and cloth and plush body portions made by Knickerbocker Toy Co., Inc. 9 inches tall (23cm) in the seated position. *Wanda Lodwick Collection.*

BELOW: Illustration 147. 21 inch (53cm) all-vinyl *Kewpie* on the *Miss Peep* body, an original design by Joseph Kallus for the *Miss Peep* doll that was also used for some Cameo *Kewpies*. *Wanda Lodwick Collection.*

OPPOSITE PAGE: Illustration 148. *Kewpie* on *Miss Peep* body (original to the doll). These hinge joints are the most unattractive design that Joseph Kallus created in his long doll designing career, although when dressed the doll can assume some cute positions. *Wanda Lodwick Collection.*

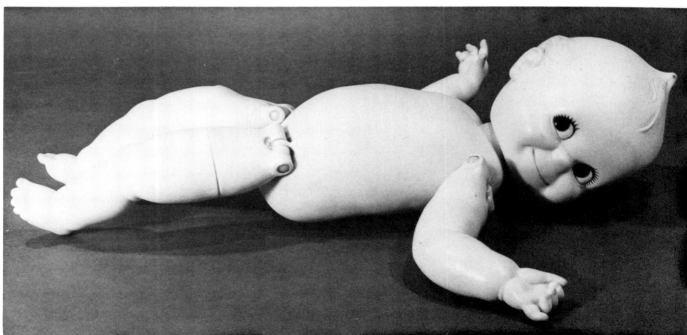

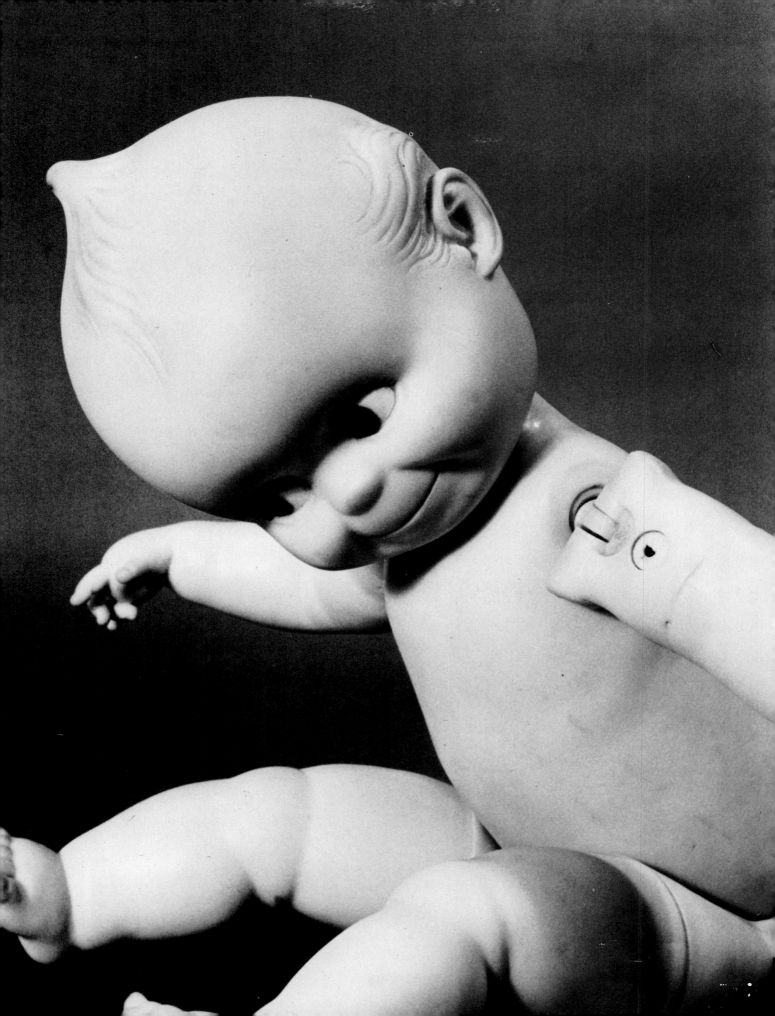

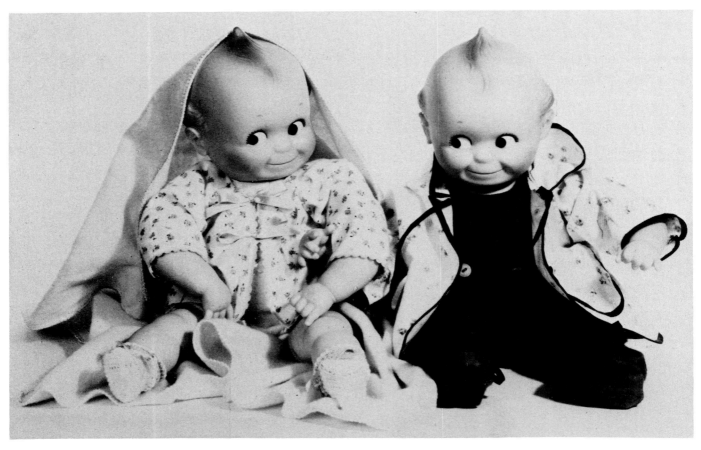

Illustration 149. Original *Kewpies* on the body that was first used for *Miss Peep.*

Illustration 150. 8½ inch (22cm) and 12 inch (31cm) *Kewpie Gal.* These dolls have molded hair and the ribbon across the head fits into slits on either side. The doll looks cute, but it is a shame to do this to *Kewpie!* The bodies are fully-jointed and are standard *Kewpie* bodies.

Illustrations 151 and **152.** 12 inch (31cm) *Kewpie Gals* in all-vinyl. Factory samples from Amsco.

cameo® doll products

6818 · 6212 · 6816 · 6181 · 6057 · 6053 · 6108 · 6004 · 6208 · 6116

THE TRADITIONAL KEWPIE® DOLL, CREATED BY *Rose O'Neill*

6004 4" SITTING KEWPIE® Kewpie in the classic "Thinker Pose". Made of soft, washable vinyl with cooing voice. Each on card. 1 dz. to carton. Weight 2 lbs.

6053 3" HO-HO® GOOD LUCK DOLL He'll bring love, luck and laughter. Laughing voice. Rub belly for good luck. Carded 1 dz. to carton. Weight 3 lbs.

6057 7" HO-HO® GOOD LUCK DOLL Same as above in 7" size. Each in see-thru canister. 1 dz. to carton. Weight 11 lbs.

6108 8" RAGSY© KEWPIE® Washable vinyl doll in red and blue. Coos and cries. 2 dz. to carton. Weight 10 lbs.

6116 6" KEWPIE SLEEPER® Popular Kewpie Doll dressed in assorted-flannel pajamas. Made of soft washable vinyl. Carded 1 dz. to carton. Weight 3 lbs.

6181 11" KEWPIE SLEEPER® Same as above in 11" size. Each in display box. 1 dz. to carton. Weight 7 lbs.

6208 8" KUDDLY KEWPIE® Toddler doll made of soft washable vinyl. Moveable arms, legs and head. Famous top knot and cooing voice. Adorable dresses with shoes and stockings. Each in a see thru canister. 1 dz. to carton. Weight 9 lbs.

6212 12" KUDDLY KEWPIE® Same as 6208 in 12" Size. Each in a colorful display box. 1 dz. to carton. Weight 13 lbs.

6816 16" MISS PEEP® The most realistic baby doll ever born. Hug her and she coos, pinch her and she cries. Exclusive "Life-Movement Joints". Made of soft washable vinyl. Dressed in a kimona, diaper and a receiving blanket tied with a wide satin sash. Tiny Knitted booties ties with a bow. Each in a colored display box. 6 each to carton. Weight 16 lbs.

6818 18" MISS PEEP® Same as above in 18" size. 6 each to carton. Weight 20 lbs.

CAMEO® DOLL PRODUCTS, DIVISION OF STROMBECKER CORP., CHICAGO, ILL. 60624 (312) 638-1000

Illustration 153. Catalog sheet from Strombecker Corp. showing the line of Cameo Doll Products. (Note: the *Kuddly Kewpie* in all-vinyl is not the same *Kuddly Kewpie* as made by Knickerbocker, which was a soft bodied doll with a vinyl face.

Illustration 154. 11 inch (28cm) *Kewpie Sleepers* from Strombecker, 1969-1973. Only the head is jointed. The original packages are shrink-wrapped cardboard boxes with an open front. The white version is Stock No. 6181; the black version is Stock No. 6191. *Author's Collection.*

144

Illustration 155. 8½ inch (22cm) *Kewpie Gal* in the original Strombecker package, Item No. 6309, 1969-1973. All-vinyl and fully-jointed. The painted hair is brown and the inserted ribbon is blue velvet. Note that this doll does not have shoes. *Author's Collection.*

BELOW LEFT: Illustration 156. 1975 *Kewpies* by Amsco, a Milton Bradley Company. Both Strombecker and Amsco advertised dolls that were designed by Joseph L. Kallus as "Cameo Exclusive Products," including wording on the original packages. Top row, from left to right: 11 inch (28cm) with jointed head and 12 inch (31cm) *Kewpie Gal*. Bottom row, from left to right: 8 inch (20cm) *Ragsy Kewpie*, (Note original package; some of the Amsco *Kewpies* were presented this way.), 8 inch (20cm) fully-jointed; 6 inch (15cm) with a jointed head, and the 4 inch (10cm) *Kewpie Thinker*, called *Kewpie Love* by Amsco.

BELOW RIGHT: Illustration 157. From the 1975 Amsco catalog. Top row, from left to right: 16 inch (41cm) fully-jointed; 14 inch (36cm) fully-jointed; 12 inch (31cm) fully-jointed; and 27 inch (69cm) fully-jointed, the largest *Kewpie* doll ever made. The bottom row shows the same dolls as the top row, wearing different costumes.

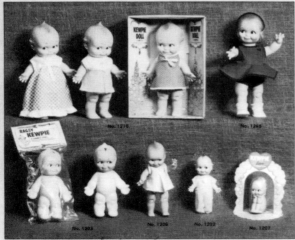

The Cameo World of Kewpie and Miss Peep

When you think of dolls, think first of the Cameo World of Kewpie and Miss Peep. Here, you'll find a universally recognized collection of high-quality dolls that have been winning the hearts of girls young and old for three generations. Only Amsco makes genuine Kewpie and Miss Peep dolls... and there are thousands of doll lovers who aren't willing to settle for anything less.

4" KEWPIE LOVE No. 1207
A one-piece soft vinyl doll, packaged in her own plastic dome surrounded by an arbor of hearts.
Individual Package Size: 6½" x 5¼" x 4¾"
Master Pack: 24   Weight per Master: 3 lbs.

6" KEWPIE No. 1202
A one-piece soft vinyl doll, dressed in a sleeper.
Individual Card Size: 10½" x 6" (blister pack)
Master Pack: 24   Weight per Master: 6 lbs.

8" KEWPIE No. 1206
A fully jointed doll with colorful play dress, stockings and shoes.
Individual Box Size: 9¾" x 5¼" x 2½"
Master Pack: 6   Weight per Master: 7 lbs.

8" KEWPIE RAGSY No. 1203
A one-piece soft vinyl doll with moveable head.
Individual Poly Bag Size: 5-3/8" x 11" (with header).
Master Pack: 24   Weight per Master: 8 lbs.

11" KEWPIE UNDRESSED (not shown) No. 1205
Create your own outfit for this pretty lady. One-piece soft vinyl body with moveable head.
Individual Poly Bag Size: 7½" x 15" (with header).
Master Pack: 12   Weight per Master: 11 lbs.

11" KEWPIE No. 1210
One-piece soft vinyl body with moveable head. In three different outfits: party dress, play suit, nightgown. Packed 4 each of 3.
Individual Box Size: 11-1/8" x 8-3/8" x 3-3/8"
Master Pack: 12   Weight per Master: 13 lbs.

12" KEWPIE GAL No. 1265
A delightful young miss version of Kewpie with hair ribbon, molded brown hair, stockings and shoes, and a colorful play dress. Fully jointed 5-piece body, moveable head.
Individual Box Size: 12" x 8¼" x 3½"
Master Pack: 6   Weight per Master: 8 lbs.

Cameo Exclusive Products, Inc., TM Licensor
© Joseph L. Kallus 1975

The Cameo World of Kewpie and Miss Peep

12" KEWPIE No. 1220
A fully jointed doll with 5-piece body and moveable head. In three different outfits: party dress, play suit, nightgown. Packed 4 each of 3.
Individual Box Size: 12-1/8" x 8-3/8" x 3-5/8"
Master Pack: 12   Weight per Master: 15 lbs.

14" KEWPIE No. 1230
A fully jointed doll with 5-piece body and moveable head. In three different outfits: party dress, play suit, nightgown. Packed 2 each of 3.
Individual Box Size: 14-3/8" x 8-7/8" x 4"
Master Pack: 6   Weight per Master: 11 lbs.

16" KEWPIE No. 1240
A fully jointed doll with 5-piece body and moveable head. In three different outfits: party dress, play suit, nightgown. Packed 2 each of 3.
Individual Box Size: 17" x 9-7/8" x 4-5/8".
Master Pack: 6   Weight per Master: 16 lbs.

27" KEWPIE No. 1250
The biggest, loveliest Kewpie of all. Fully jointed 5-piece body with moveable head.
Individual Box Size: 27-1/8" x 12" x 7".
Master Pack: 4   Weight per Master: 20 lbs.

Cameo Exclusive Products, Inc., TM Licensor
© Joseph L. Kallus 1975

MISS PEEP DOLLS
Both Miss Peep dolls come complete with pink receiving blanket, white kimono, nightie, cotton tie diaper, stockings and booties. Both are fully jointed with moveable head.

16" MISS PEEP No. 1281
Individual Box Size: 16-7/8" x 10-5/8" x 3-7/8"
Master Pack: 6   Weight per Master: 12 lbs.

18" MISS PEEP No. 1282
Individual Box Size: 19-7/8" x 14-5/8" x 4½"
Master Pack: 6   Weight per Master: 18 lbs.

Illustration 158. All-vinyl and fully-jointed Amsco *Kewpie*, ca. 1973, in the original box in the 12 inch (31cm) size. The Amsco packages are like the ones from Strombecker and are a cardboard box with an open front covered in shrink-wrap. The gold label on the right front tells that this doll is "Celebrating Kewpie's 60th Birthday." The original price of $5.78 is on the upper right-hand corner of the box. *Author's Collection.*

OPPOSITE PAGE: Illustration 159. 8 inch (20cm) fully-jointed all-vinyl *Kewpie* from Amsco, ca. 1973, dressed in an original old-fashioned costume to celebrate Kewpie's 60th birthday. *Author's Collection.*

Illustration 160. Hang tag for Jesco *Kewpies.*

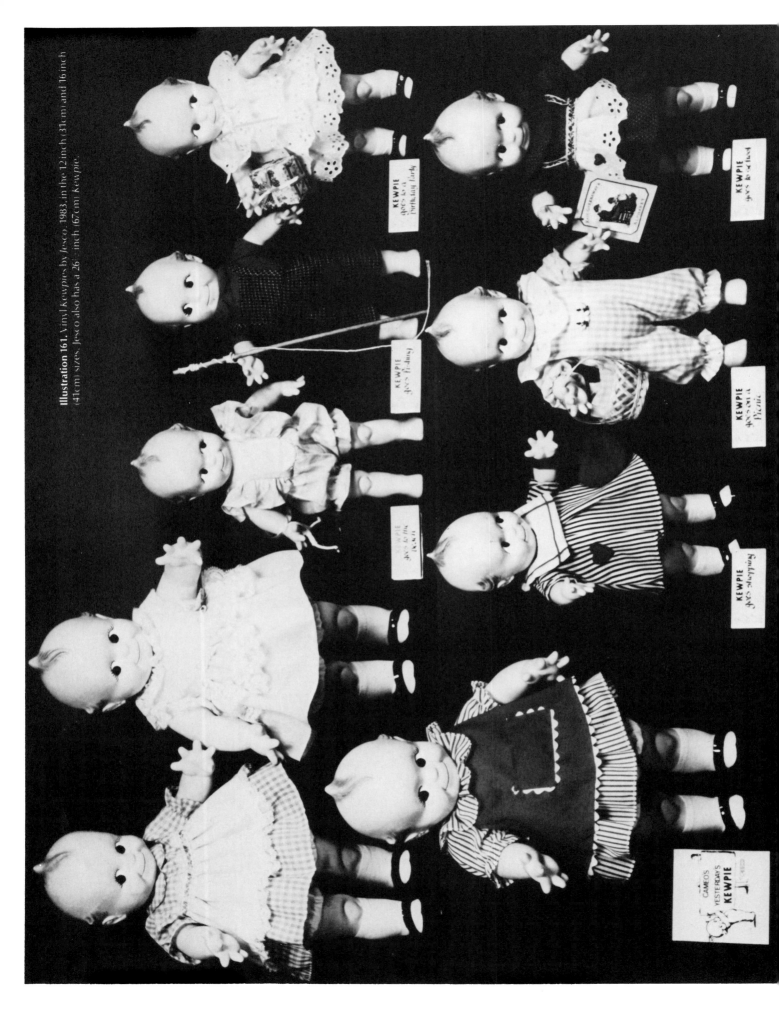

Illustration 161. Vinyl Kewpies by Jesco, 1983, in the 12-inch (31cm) and 16-inch (41cm) sizes. Jesco also has a 26¼-inch (67cm) Kewpie.

SCOOTLES

Composition

ca. 1929+

Cameo Doll Co.; distributed by others, including Effanbee

Jointed arms, legs and head; painted eyes or sleep eyes; painted hair.

8	inches (20cm)	14	inches (36cm)
9½	inches (24cm)	15½	inches (39cm)
12	inches (31cm)	21	inches (53cm)

All-bisque

ca. 1929+

Made in Germany; Made in Japan

Jointed only at arms.

Sizes:

5 to 6 inches (13 to 15cm)

Cloth

ca. 1930s

Sizes:

10 inches (25cm);
18½ inches (47cm); and others

Vinyl

1964+

Cameo Doll Co.; Jesco, Inc.

Sizes:

10	inches	(25cm)
12	inches	(31cm)
14	inches	(36cm)
16	inches	(41cm) with sleep eyes

Illustration 162. All-composition and fully-jointed *Scootles* with painted and molded hair and painted eyes. 1930s.

Illustration 163. All-composition *Scootles* in original outfits. 1930s.

LEFT: Illustration 164. 8 inch (20cm) all-composition and fully-jointed *Scootles* with painted hair and painted eyes. No marks. *Patricia N. Schoonmaker Collection.*

Illustration 165. Boy and girl all-composition and fully-jointed *Scootles*, 1940s. This is the largest size composition *Scootles* and is 21 inches (53cm). The girl has green sleep, side-glancing eyes; the boy has brown sleep, side-glancing eyes. *Helen Sieverling Collection.*

Illustration 166. Close-up of boy *Scootles* with side-glancing brown sleep eyes. *Helen Sieverling Collection.*

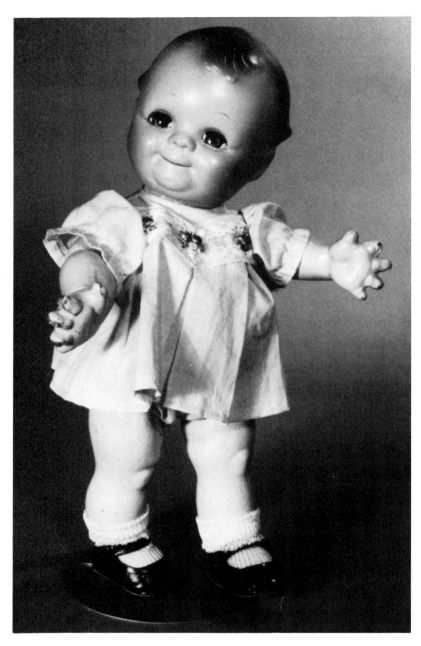

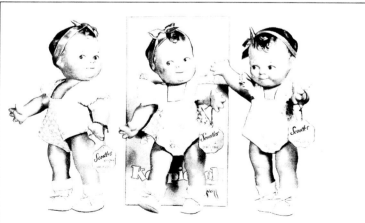

Illustration 167. All-composition *Scootles* that is a rare original combination of a different *Scootles* face on a *Kewpie* body. This doll came from Joseph Kallus' samples. *Helen Sieverling Collection.*

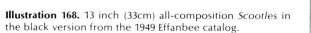

Illustration 168. 13 inch (33cm) all-composition *Scootles* in the black version from the 1949 Effanbee catalog.

3434CR—Colored Scootles: 13" doll. Sunsuit costume, colored ribbon bow. Fully jointed with movable head. Shoes and socks. Individually packaged in display box. 2 doz. to carton.

Illustration 169. 12½ inch (32cm) all-composition and fully-jointed *Scootles* in a black version with painted hair and eyes. The costume is original. This is the doll shown in the 1949 Effanbee catalog. *Helen Sieverling Collection.*

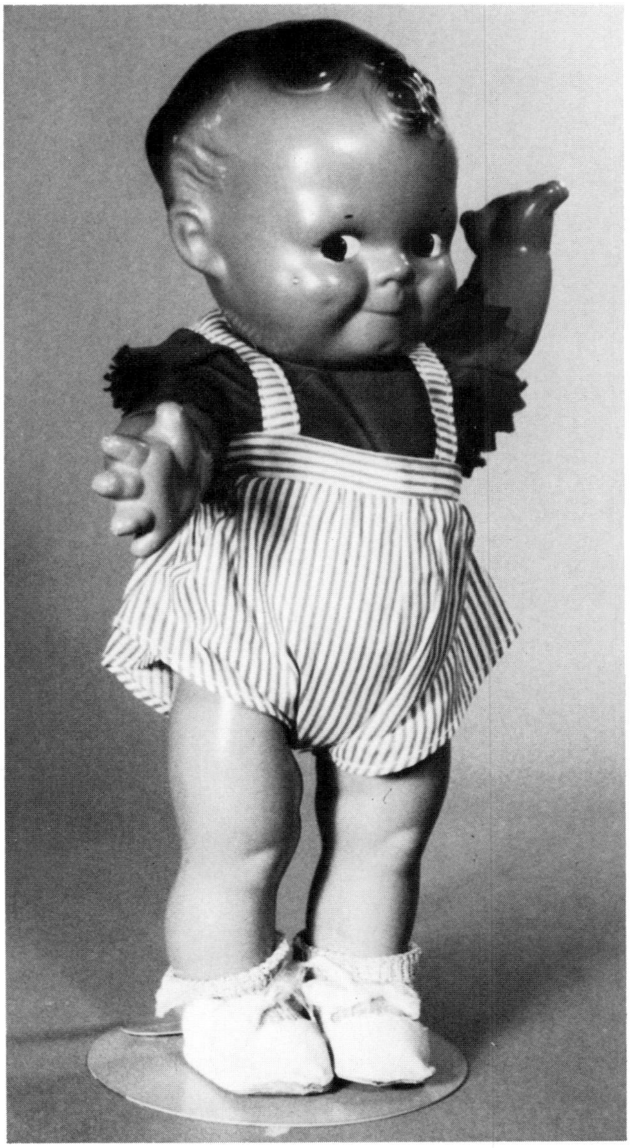

Illustration 170. 16 inch (41cm) all-composition and fully-jointed *Scootles* from the 1949 Effanbee doll catalog.

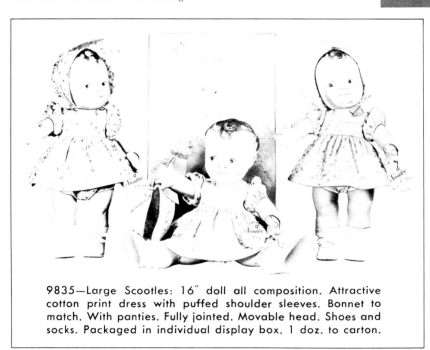

9835—Large Scootles: 16″ doll all composition. Attractive cotton print dress with puffed shoulder sleeves. Bonnet to match. With panties. Fully jointed. Movable head. Shoes and socks. Packaged in individual display box. 1 doz. to carton.

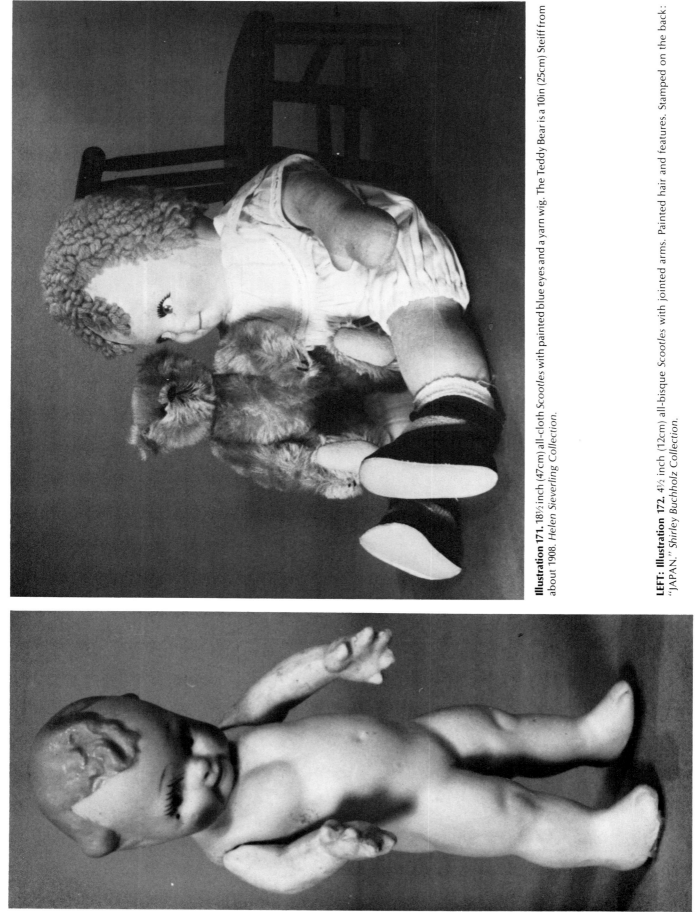

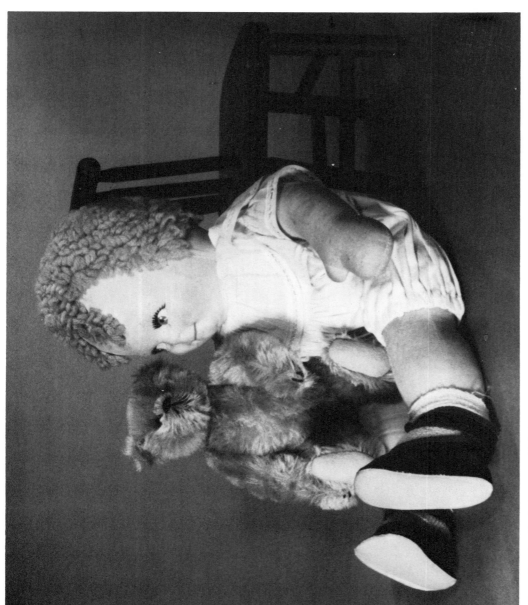

Illustration 171. 18½ inch (47cm) all-cloth *Scootles* with painted blue eyes and a yarn wig. The Teddy Bear is a 10in (25cm) Steiff from about 1908. *Helen Sieverling Collection.*

LEFT: Illustration 172. 4½ inch (12cm) all-bisque *Scootles* with jointed arms. Painted hair and features. Stamped on the back: "JAPAN." *Shirley Buchholz Collection.*

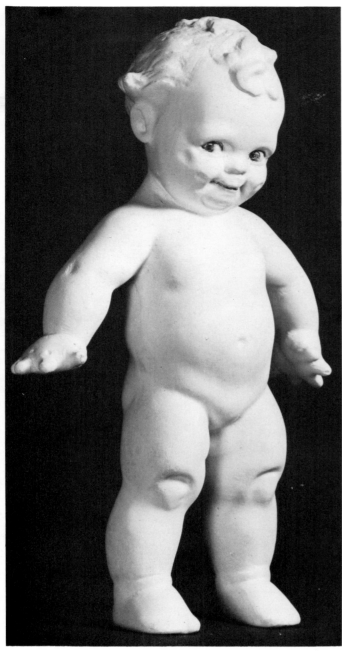

Illustration 173. Plaster model for molding the vinyl *Scootles* in the 1960s by Joseph L. Kallus. Note that this figure does not include doll's joints yet.

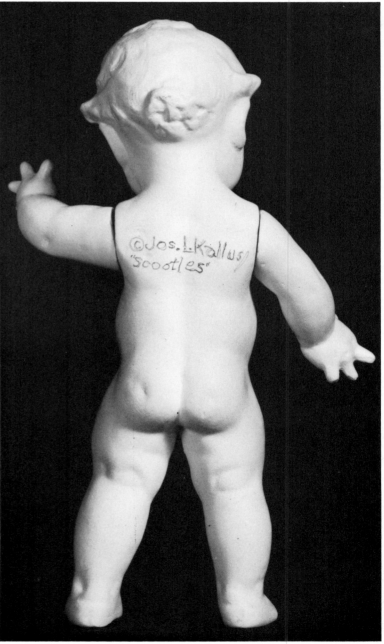

Illustration 174. Back view of a plaster model by Joseph L. Kallus for casting a vinyl *Scootles*. This sample has the arms cut for the jointed position.

Illustrations 176, 177 and **178.** Vinyl *Scootles* from the 1960s and 1970s in the four sizes, showing original costumes.

Illustrations 179 and **180.** 16 inch (41cm) vinyl *Scootles*, 1960s-1970s, with sleep eyes and molded hair.

HO-HO

In 1940 Rose O'Neill created *Ho-Ho*, the Little Laughing Buddha. This was a figure with no moving parts, but it is best described as a doll. By 1941 plaster figures of *Ho-Ho* were marketed by Cameo. Rose O'Neill was always interested in the exotic and she was fascinated by Oriental motifs. She must have thought that her Ho-Ho was a delightful creation that would charm children and adults as Kewpie had at the beginning of the century. In retrospect, Ho-Ho was an unfortunate choice of a Rose O'Neill item to manufacture as this design caused controversy and offended many people.

In 1965 Kallus began producing vinyl, soap and jewelry Ho-Hos. Remco carried two sizes of the vinyl doll (actually a one-piece figure). On October 14, 1965, Kallus received the following letter from Rev. Takashi Tsuji, the National Director of the Bureau of Buddhist Education of the Buddhist Churches of America:

"We have on hand a rubber doll (sic) of the image of Buddha which is sold as a toy.

As you know the image of Buddha is sacred to five hundred and fifty million Buddhists throughout the world.

The rubber image as designed by your firm is most undignified and we feel that this representation desecrates the object of our worship. We are sure you will understand the reaction you will receive if you were to produce dolls of other spiritual leaders of world religions in this manner. We sincerely hope, therefore, that you will take appropriate steps to take this article off the market.

We would be very grateful if you will inform us what steps will be taken."

Joseph Kallus' reply of October 20, 1965:

"We regret that our "Ho-Ho" (sic) figure make (sic) the impression you describe. However we will give serious consideration to your statements and we will inform you of the decision of our Board of Directors."

Part of a letter from Kallus of November 10, 1965, informing the Bureau of Buddhist Education of the Cameo decision:

"The word "Buddah" (sic) will be expunged from all our records and removed from all our literature, labels, tags, etc., etc. when re-ordering of said printed matter or items.

Our sculpted figure "Ho-Ho" was conceived by the world famous artist, Rose O'Neill, and it was copy-righted and trade-marked in the Library of Congress, Washington, D.C.

We trust the above action will be satisfactory."

The plaster *Ho-Ho* of the 1940s is 6¼ inch (16cm) tall.
The vinyl *Ho-Ho* of 1965 is 3 inch (8cm), 5 inch (13cm) and 7 inches (18cm) tall.

Illustration 181. At left is the plaster *Ho-Ho* from 1941. It is 6¼ inches (16cm) tall and is painted in bright colors. Incised on the back: "HO-HO / ROSE O'NEILL / ©1940." At the right is the vinyl *Ho-Ho*, the Little Laughing Buddha, of 1965 in the 3 inch (8cm) size. It is brown vinyl with white painted teeth. Back marked "ROSE O'NEILL / © / JLK / CAMEO." *Helen Sieverling Collection.*

OPPOSITE PAGE: Illustration 182. Joseph Kallus' original model for *Ho-Ho*, or possibly one of the original plaster versions of the 1940s.

Illustration 183. The vinyl *Ho-Ho* of 1965. This figure came in sizes of 3 inches (7cm), 5 inches (13cm) and 7 inches (18cm).

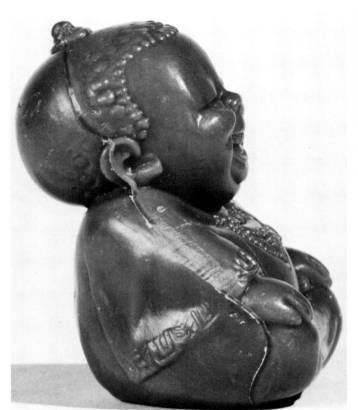

Illustrations 184 and **185.** Soap Ho-Ho.

Illustration 186. Three plaster versions of *Ho-Ho* that were Joseph Kallus' models and a Ho-Ho jewelry item on a chain.

JOSEPH L. KALLUS DOLLS

Joseph L. Kallus created many different dolls from 1912 to the late 1960s. Many of them were a Kallus execution of another artist's design; several of them were Kallus' own designs. Joseph Kallus lost many of his records of the early dolls and dates were often established later from imperfect memories and improper research. Many doll books and articles show the doll designs of Joseph L. Kallus. The date given for the doll is usually the copyright date rather than the date the doll was produced. A case in point is Popeye. This character was copyrighted in 1932 by King Features Syndicate. The dolls were not made until the 1940s. Scootles was copyrighted in 1925; the dolls were not produced until at least 1929. A doll could be made before it was copyrighted also. Kewpie was made in 1912, but it was not copyrighted until 1913. Felix the Cat was copyrighted in 1922 by Pat Sullivan; the Kallus *Felix* dates from about 1928 according to his files. If the date of a doll is not known to be accurate, it is given as *ca.* plus the date.

KING FEAT. SYND.   12½" TALL

LUCKY JEEP

This comic little animal with a "Durante Schnozzola" is a real hot item. Colored bright yellow with touches of red in the right spots and a patch of white on tummy. Can be twisted into the funniest positions. The head, arms, legs and tail are segmented. A whopping favorite on every counter.

Retails for $1.00
YOUR PRICE 7.20 Dozen

Packed in individual boxes and shipped 3 doz. to ctn.

KING FEAT. SYND.   14½" TALL

POPEYE

Adored by millions of children who see him in the movies, read him in the comic strips and hear him on the radio. The Popeye doll is a honey of a novelty item that sells on sight. Very colorful and is constructed with the famous patented wood segmented construction. Can assume 1000 and one positions. Loads of fun for adult fans, too.

Retails for $1.00
YOUR PRICE 7.20 Dozen

Packed in individual boxes and shipped 4 doz. to ctn.

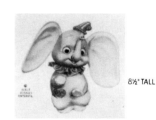

WALT DISNEY ENTERPRISES   8½" TALL

DUMBO

The sweetest, most appealing of Walt Disney's famous movie characters, currently winning the hearts of millions of movie fans—adults as well as children. Dumbo's large ears flap, head and trunk are fully jointed and can be turned into many humorous positions. Body is elephant grey with colorful ribbon around neck and yellow moulded clown hat on head. CELLULOID EYES with black, moving pupils.

Retails for $1.00
YOUR PRICE 7.20 Dozen

Packed in individual boxes and shipped 4 doz. to ctn.

10½" TALL

PETE

Made with the patented wood segmented construction, this lively little fellow gives countless hours of pleasure. You can bend and twist him into innumerable comical positions. Very appealing face and colorfully painted. Red body, arms and nose, white face with black ears, yellow tips for hands, black legs and orange feet.

Retails for $1.00
YOUR PRICE 7.20 Dozen

Packed in individual boxes and shipped 4 doz. to ctn.

KING FEAT. SYND.   13½" TALL

Little Annie Rooney

There's hardly a little girl who doesn't know Annie Roonie and who wouldn't love this striking likeness of this famous character. Big sales all over the country prove Annie Roonie a "bellringer". Tastefully dressed in attractive simple assorted style costumes.

Retails for $1.00
YOUR PRICE 7.20 Dozen

Packed in individual boxes and shipped 4 doz. to ctn.

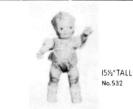

15½" TALL No. 532

Rose O'Neill's SCOOTLES

Retails for $2.00
YOUR PRICE 14.40 Dozen

Packed in individual boxes and shipped 2 doz. to ctn.

Popular creation of Rose O'Neill, famous for years as the top ranking author and illustrator of best selling children's books and the creator of the internationally well-known KEWPIE DOLLS.

Exquisitely modelled, these Scootles dolls are Rose O'Neill's gems! Sturdily constructed for plenty of play hours. Delightfully dressed in assorted romper styles with fine quality shoes and silk stockings.

12½" TALL No. 332

Rose O'Neill's SCOOTLES

Retails for $1.00
YOUR PRICE 7.20 Dozen

Packed in individual boxes and shipped 3 doz. to ctn.

4¾" tall
3¼" wide
2½" deep

IVORY ANTIQUE   BRONZE ANTIQUE

Gen. Mac Arthur BANK

This smart looking bank is one of the leading General MacArthur items now on the market. General MacArthur's striking profile is sculptured in relief on both front and back with the inspiring slogan—"Save For Victory"—"Liberty". Timely, popularly priced, with a patriotic purpose. Made of durable wood pulp composition and handsomely finished in ivory or bronze antique.

Opening accommodates nickels, dimes, quarters and bills. Capacity approximately $50.00 in nickels. Wrapped in individual cardboard sleeves and shipped ¼ doz. and 1 gross to carton.

Retails for 30¢
YOUR PRICE 25.80 Gross

CAMEO DOLL PRODUCTS CO.,   PORT ALLEGANY, PA.

Illustration 187. Cameo Doll Products Co. catalog from about 1942. Note: The sizes given in doll catalogs are seldom accurate.

BABY BUNDIE	1918	All-composition with jointed arms; mohair wig; painted features	12	inches	(31cm)
		All-composition; fully-jointed	16	inches	(41cm)
BO-FAIR	1919				
DOLLIE	1921				
VANITIE	1921				
BABY BO-KAYE	ca. 1925	Bisque, composition, celluloid heads; cloth body; usually composition arms and legs	16	inches	(41cm)
			18	inches	(46cm)
			20	inches	(51cm)
		All-bisque; fully-jointed	6	inches	(15cm)
BYE-LO BABY	ca. 1926	Composition head; cloth body			
LITTLE ANNIE ROONEY (ROONIE)	ca. 1926	All-composition; fully-jointed from Jack Collins cartoon	13½	inches	(34cm)
			16	inches	(41cm)
BABY BLOSSOM	ca. 1927	Composition head, arms, legs; cloth body. (Looks very similar to Effanbee's Bubbles)	20	inches	(51cm)
FELIX THE CAT	ca. 1928	All wood segments jointed with elastic	3½	inches	(9cm)
			8½	inches	(22cm)
		Copyright by Pat Sullivan	13	inches	(33cm)
BONZO (dog)	ca. 1928	Composition. Could be sold to the Carnival Trade only as per contract with Geo. Borgfeldft. Royalty to be paid was 10%; sale price to jobbers was $12.00 per dozen.	12 to 14	inches	(31 to 36cm)
SISSIE	1928				
MARGIE	1929	Composition head; segmented wood body	5	inches	(13cm)
			9½	inches	(24cm)
PINKIE	1930	Similar to Margie with a baby head			
RCA RADIOTRON	1930	Also called The Selling Fool. Composition head with a hat that is a radio tube; body segmented wood	15½	inches	(39cm)
BETTY BOOP	1932	Composition head; segmented wood arms and legs; molded composition torso	12	inches	(31cm)
JOY	1932	Similar to Margie with a molded loop on head for a hair ribbon			
MARCIA	1933	All-composition girl with molded hair; painted features			
BANDMASTER (BANDY)	1935	Advertising figure for General Electric			
MR. PEANUT	1935	Composition and wood segments			
SANTA	ca. 1935	Advertising figure for Shaeffer Pen Co.	9½	inches	(24cm)
BABY SNOOKS	1939	Composition head and hands; wood feet; coiled wire body. Made by Ideal	12	inches	(31cm)
CROWNIE	1940	Composition head; segmented wood body			
PINOCCHIO	1940	Composition head; segmented body Made by Ideal	8	inches	(20cm)
			11	inches	(28cm)
			20	inches	(51cm)
			9	inches	(23cm)
JIMINY CRICKET	1940	Wood segments. Made by Ideal Pinocchio and Jiminy Cricket are Walt Disney Designs			
CHAMP	1942	All-composition boy doll	16	inches	(41cm)
DUMBO	1942	Composition; head and trunk jointed; rubber ears. A Walt Disney Design	8½	inches	(22cm)
PETE THE PUP	ca. 1942	Composition head; jointed wood segment body	10½	inches	(27cm)
POPEYE	1942	Composition head; jointed wood segment body	14½	inches	(37cm)

JEEP	1942	Composition and fully-jointed; wood segment tail	9 inches	(23cm)
			12½ inches	(32cm)
		Popeye and Jeep were licensed by King Features Syndicate		
GIGGLES	1946	All-composition; fully-jointed; molded hair loop for bow	13 inches	(33cm)
HOWDY DOODY	1947	Composition head; jointed wood segment body. Made by Noma Electric (Effanbee)	13 inches	(33cm)
SUPERMAN	late 1940s	Made like Howdy Doody		
PINKIE	1950s	All-vinyl and fully-jointed with rooted hair	27 inches	(69cm)
BABY	1950s	Vinyl head; magic skin arms and legs; cloth body; inset eyes	17½ inches	(45cm)
DYP-A-BABE	1956	All-vinyl and fully-jointed drink and wet feature		
FELIX THE CAT	late 1950s	All-vinyl and fully-jointed		
POPEYE	1957-1959	All-vinyl and fully-jointed		
PEANUT	1958	All-vinyl and fully-jointed; drink and wet feature	18½ inches	(47cm)
MARGIE	1958	All-vinyl and fully-jointed; rooted hair; sleep eyes	17 inches	(43cm)
BABY MINE	1961	All-vinyl and fully-jointed	18 inches	(46cm)
MISS PEEP	1969	All-vinyl and fully-jointed with hinge joints; painted hair and eyes	16 inches	(41cm)
			18½ inches	(47cm)
			20 inches	(51cm)

Illustrations 188 and **189.** It is not known if these dogs designed by Joseph L. Kallus were placed into production. They have composition heads and wooden segmented bodies that are strung together with elastic. They are fabulous!

Illustration 190. Joseph L. Kallus' first doll was *Baby Bundie*. She is 12 inches (31cm) tall; all-composition with jointed arms only. Note the space between the legs. The eyes are painted and the wig is mohair. Paper label on bottom of feet: "DES. REG. XXCIII 512 / by J.L. KALLUS / BUN © DIE." *Helen Sieverling Collection.*

OPPOSITE PAGE: Illustration 191. *Margie* dolls from a window display, 1930s.

Illustration 192. *Margie* from about 1929. The composition head has painted features and molded hair. The body is made from wooden segments that are like large beads and they are strung together with elastic.

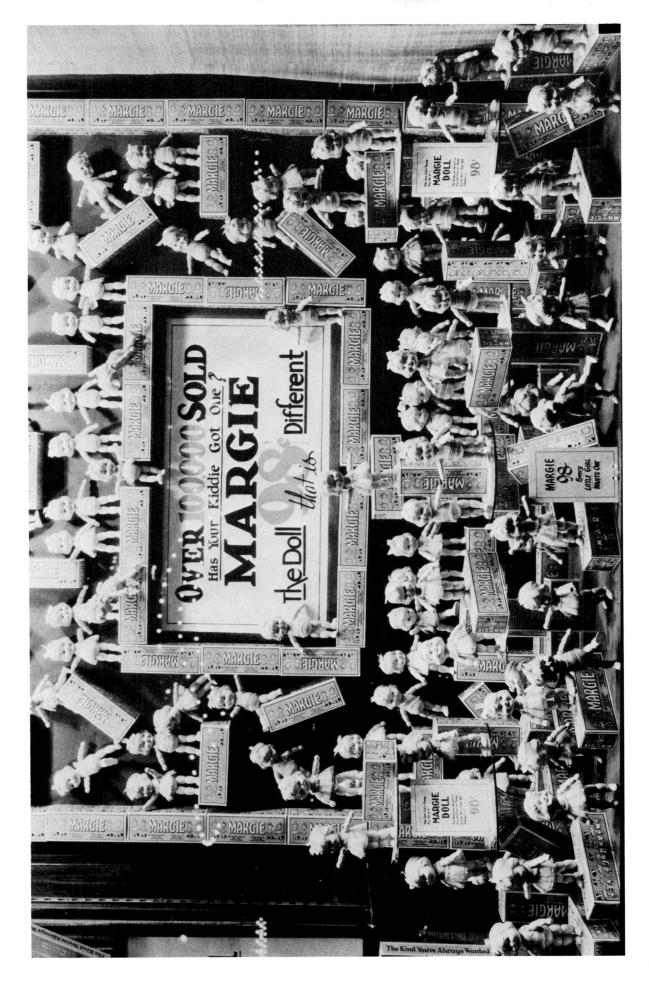

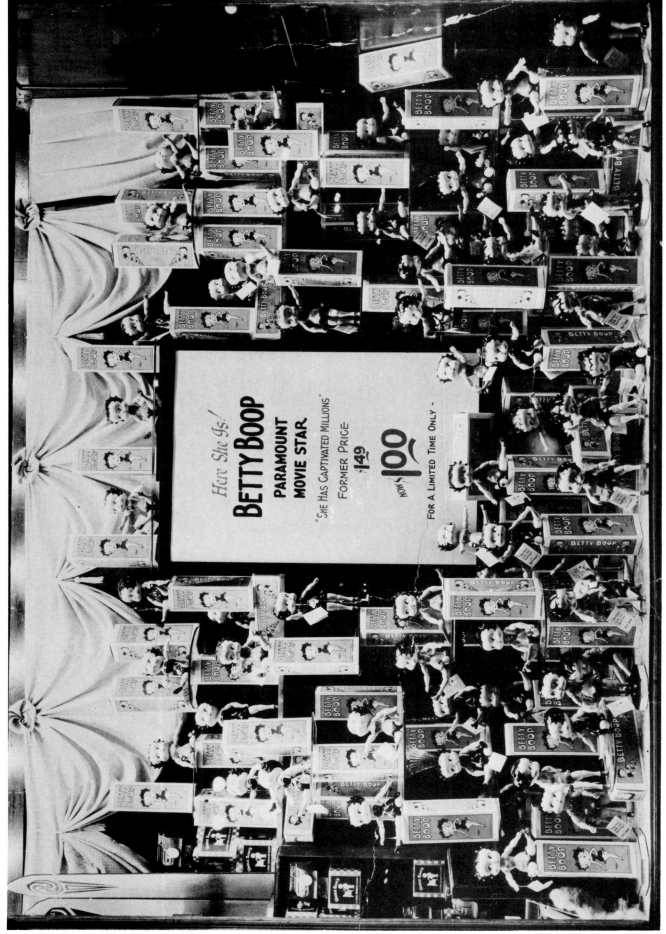

Inside the image:

Here She Is!
BETTY BOOP
PARAMOUNT
MOVIE STAR

"She Has Captivated Millions"

FORMER PRICE
$149

NOW $100

FOR A LIMITED TIME ONLY —

Illustration 193. *Betty Boop* window display from the 1930s.

Illustration 194. *Joy* window display from the 1930s.

Illustration 195 and **196.** *Marcia*, circa 1933, an all-composition doll with molded hair and painted features. Note the molded shoes.

Illustration 197. Original Kallus artwork for *Crownie*, 1940s.

BELOW: Illustration 198 and **199.** *Crownie* with a composition head and a wooden body.

Illustration 200. 11 inch (28cm) *Pinocchio* and 9 inch (23cm) *Jiminy Cricket* by Ideal, 1940, with *Pinocchio's* original box. This is the design used in the Walt Disney animated movie. The doll design is an original by Joseph L. Kallus: *Pinocchio's* head is composition, as is the torso; his arms and legs are elastic joined wooden segments. *Jiminy Cricket* is all-wood of a similar construction. *Author's Collection.*

Illustration 201. *Champ*, an all-composition body doll, 16 inches (41cm) tall and fully-jointed. Cameo Doll Products Co. catalog from about 1942.

POPEYE
an all time favorite Comic Strip

A NATION-WIDE TELEVISION STAR
Comes to Life now
in a VINYL DOLL

No.27 - Fully jointed, ball and socket type. Can assume 1000 and one positions

HE SITS
HE RUNS
HE KICKS
HE TILTS HIS HEAD
HE RAISES and POSES HIS ARMS
HE WHISTLES HIS VINYL PIPE

He's the MOST Life-like and Realistic DOLL you EVER SOLD !

CAMEO DOLL PRODUCTS CO., INC.
Port Allegany, Pennsylvania

13½" Tall

TO RETAIL AT $3.98
YOUR PRICE $28.80 PER DOZ.
PACKED IN INDIVIDUAL WINDOW BOX
2 DOZ. TO MASTER SHIPPING CARTON.
WEIGHT OF CARTON ABOUT 27
POUNDS F.O.B. PORT ALLEGANY, PA.

Illustration 202. Original advertising for vinyl *Popeye*, late 1950s.

Illustration 204. 9 inch (23cm) *Jeep*, the dog from Popeye, 1940s. All-composition with wooden segments for the tail and arms and legs. Note that the *Jeep* in the advertising copy is all-composition. *Jeep* is a light yellow color.

Leading Comic Strip Characters Come To Life - - In These Colorful, Well-Made, Popularly Priced Items!

... here's a tip! -- "DOLLAR ITEMS ARE TERRIFIC!"

"Gimme the Spinach"...
POPEYE
THE SAILOR MAN

14½" TALL

Adored by millions of children who see him in the movies, read him in the comic strips and hear him on the radio. The Popeye doll is a honey of a novelty item that sells on sight. Very colorful and is constructed with the famous patented wood segmented construction. Can assume 1000 and one positions. Loads of fun for adult fans, too.

RETAILS FOR $1.00

YOUR PRICE $7.20 PER DOZEN
F.O.B. PORT ALLEGANY

Packed in Individual Boxes — 4 Doz. to Carton

THE QUAINTEST, QUEEREST FUNNIEST CHARACTER... CO-STARRING WITH POPEYE..

LUCKY JEEP
THE ARMY'S MASCOT

12½" TALL

This comic little animal with a "Durante Schnozzola" is a real hot item. Colored bright yellow with touches of red in the right spots and a patch of white on tummy. Can be twisted into the funniest positions. The head, arms, legs and tail are segmented. A whopping favorite on every counter.

RETAILS FOR $1.00

YOUR PRICE $7.20 PER DOZEN
F.O.B. PORT ALLEGANY

Packed in Individual Boxes — 3 Doz. to Carton

America's Favorite
LITTLE ANNIE ROONIE

The Sweetest, Most Popular, Little Heroine of the Comic Strips

There's hardly a little girl who doesn't know Annie Roonie and who wouldn't love this striking likeness of this famous character. Big sales all over the country prove Annie Roonie a "bell-ringer". Tastefully dressed in attractive simple assorted style costumes.

13½" TALL

RETAILS FOR $1.00

YOUR PRICE $7.20 PER DOZEN
F.O.B. PORT ALLEGANY

Packed in Individual Boxes — 4 Doz. to Carton

Be Wise! — Cameo-ize with these "Cameo-Clickers" Toy Trade reports popularly priced items hot! Cash in with Cameo — for Fall!

MAIL THIS ORDER BLANK TODAY!

FILL IN, ENCLOSE IN ENVELOPE AND MAIL TODAY !

CAMEO DOLL PRODUCTS CO.
PORT ALLEGANY PA.

Please rush the following order to us.

No. 532 SCOOTLES DOLLS   at $7.20 per doz.
No. 532 SCOOTLES DOLLS   at $14.40 per doz.
POPEYE DOLLS   at $7.20 per doz.
LUCKY JEEP DOLLS   at $7.20 per doz.
LITTLE ANNIE ROONEY DOLLS   at $7.20 per doz.

Name
Address
City   State   Buyer

CAMEO DOLL PRODUCTS CO., PORT ALLEGANY, PA.

Illustration 203. Kallus designs of cartoon characters, 1940s.

173

LEFT: Illustration 205. 9½ inch (24cm) *Santa* used as an advertisement for Shaeffer pens. This design was registered in 1935, but this figure shown here is from the late 1940s. It is all-composition and is only jointed at the right arm with an open hand for gripping a Shaeffer pen. There is a large "S" on the hat, signifying Shaeffer. *Author's Collection.*

Illustration 207. 13½ inch (34cm) all-composition and fully-jointed *Giggles* with molded hair and painted blue eyes. The clothing is replaced. *Helen Sieverling Collection.*

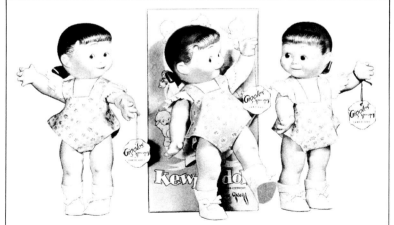

9613—Giggles: 13″ all composition doll. Attractive print sun-suit. Fully jointed. Movable arms, legs and head. Ribbon bow in back of head. Individually packaged in display box. 2 doz. to carton.

Illustration 206. *Giggles* from the 1949 Effanbee Doll Company Catalog.

CLOCKWISE: Illustration 208. 13 inch (33cm) *Howdy Doody* by Noma Electric (Effanbee), 1947. The head is composition; the body is wooden segments. The doll is not marked.

Illustration 209. Cameo Doll Products Co., Inc., advertisement from the 1960s showing *Miss Peep, Peanut* and *Kewpie Gal.*

Illustration 210. *Kewpie* in vinyl with a vinyl *Felix the Cat* from the late 1950s.

Illustrations 211 and **212.** Two versions of Kallus' *Dyp-a-Babe* from the late 1950s. This doll had a drink and wet feature like the Effanbee *Dy-Dee Baby*, which also came packed in a similar layette during the same time period.

Illustration 213. 18½ inch (47cm) all-vinyl *Peanut* from 1958. Note the extra joints at the wrists.

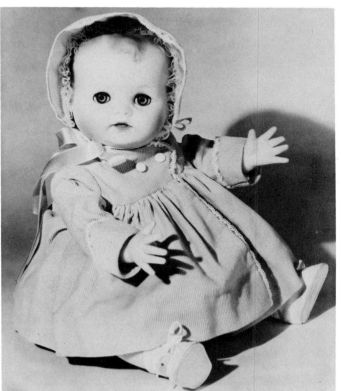

Illustrations 214 and **215.** Two versions of *Peanut*, called "Affectionately Peanut," in all-vinyl.

all VINYL
★ NEW

★ Fully jointed

★ Ball and socket
  universal joint
  type. Can assume
  1000 and one poses.

★ In segments. Split
  at waistline of body,
  arms at shoulder and
  legs at body. Head, universal joint at neckline: head will tilt and swivel in socket.

★ Rooted Soran wig.

★ Closing eyes with long hair eyelashes.

★ Dressed in fine custom made originals.

★ Hat to match.

★ Patent leather shoes and rayon socks.

  Packed in quality individual set-up boxes, one dozen to a master carton.
  Weight of carton about 32 lbs.

CAMEO DOLL PRODUCTS CO., INC.
Port Allegany, Pennsylvania

Illustration 216. Advertising copy for 17 inch (43cm) all-vinyl *Margie* of 1958.

BELOW: Illustration 217 and **218.** Two versions of Joseph Kallus' all-vinyl *Margie*, his only girl doll in this medium.

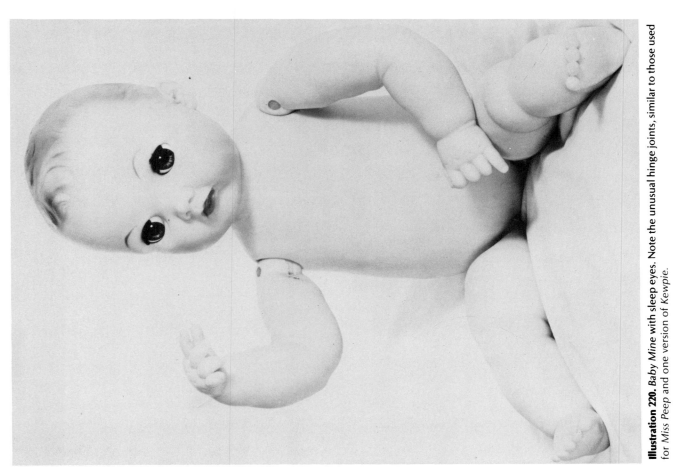

Illustration 220. *Baby Mine* with sleep eyes. Note the unusual hinge joints, similar to those used for *Miss Peep* and one version of *Kewpie*.

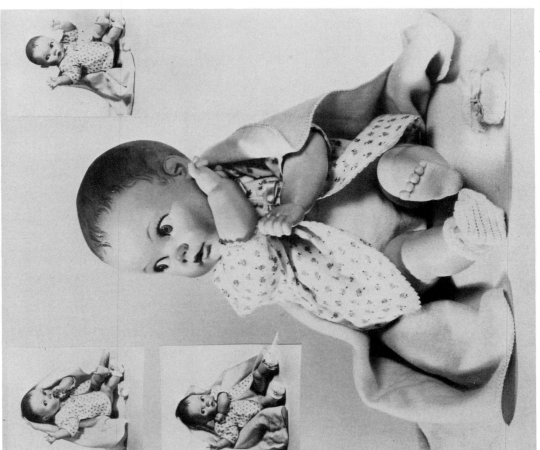

Illustration 219. 18 inch (46cm) all-vinyl and fully-jointed *Baby Mine*, 1961, with painted eyes.

ABOVE, RIGHT and OPPOSITE PAGE, LEFT: Illustrations 221, 222 and 223. All-vinyl *Miss Peep* of the late 1960s came in sizes of 16 inches (41cm), 18½ inches (47cm) and 20 inches (51cm). This is probably the last doll designed by Joseph L. Kallus.

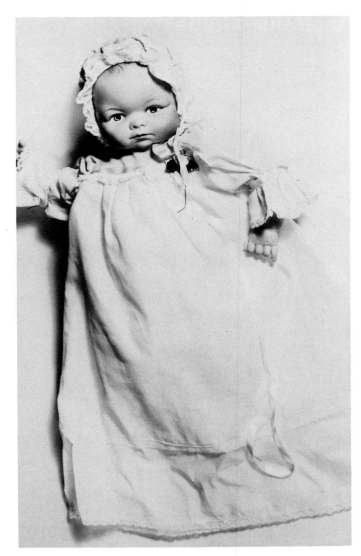

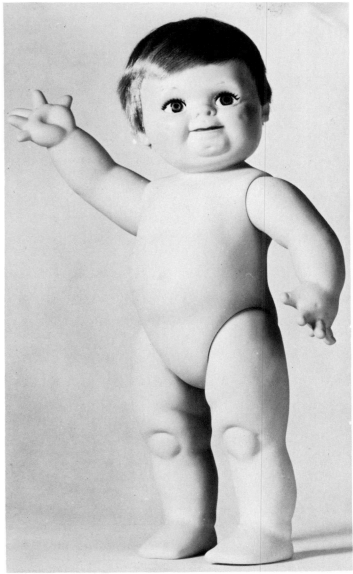

Illustration 224. Prototype doll: A vinyl *Scootles* with rooted hair and painted eyes that Kallus planned to use for a modern *Giggles*.

Kewpies Dolls & Art Value Guide

Name	Size	Material Made	Specific Type of Collectible	Year Made	Manufacturer	Current Price
Advertisement	11.75in (30cm)	Cardboard	stand-up ad featuring Kewpie with a red-flocked Santa Claus hat advertising Kewpie embroidery pictures	pre-1920		$25 – $35
Article			from Good Housekeeping, telling about the Kewpie's pet, the Kewpie dog	1915		$20 – $25
Article			from Ladies Home Journal, Kewpieville, verse and drawings by Rose O'Neill	April 1925	Rose O'Neill	$20 – $25
Article			from Ladies Home Journal, Kewpieville, verse and drawings by Rose O'Neill	December 1925	Rose O'Neill	$20 – $25
Article			from Ladies Home Journal, Kewpieville, verse and drawings by Rose O'Neill	December 1928	Rose O'Neill	$20 – $25
Article			from Ladies Home Journal, Kewpieville, verse and drawings by Rose O'Neill	May 1926	Rose O'Neill	$20 – $25
Article			from Ladies Home Journal, Kewpieville, verse and drawings by Rose O'Neill	May 1927	Rose O'Neill	$20 – $25
Article			from Ladies Home Journal, Kewpieville, verse and drawings by Rose O'Neill	September 1925	Rose O'Neill	$20 – $25
Article			from Ladies Home Journal, Kewpieville, verse and drawings by Rose O'Neill	October 1925	Rose O'Neill	$20 – $25
Article			from Woman's Home Companion - Dotty and Four of Her Kewpie Friends	July 1913	Rose O'Neill	$20 – $25
Article			from Woman's Home Companion - Dotty Darling and the Kewpies	March 1911	Rose O'Neill	$20 – $25
Article			from Woman's Home Companion - Kewpie Kutouts		Rose O'Neill	$20 – $25
Article			from Woman's Home Companion - The Flying Kewpies	May 1913	Rose O'Neill	$20 – $25
Article			from Woman's Home Companion - The Kewpies and Their New Adventures	October 1911	Rose O'Neill	$20 – $25
Article			from Woman's Home Companion - The Kewpies' Christmas Party	December 1911	Rose O'Neill	$20 – $25
Article			from Woman's Home Companion - The Kindly Kewpies: Verses and Pictures by Rose O'Neill		Rose O'Neill	$20 – $25
Article			How the Kewpie Turned into Dolls		Rose O'Neill	$20 – $25
Baby	17.5in (45cm)		vinyl head, magic skin arms and legs, cloth body, inset eyes	1950s	Joseph Kallus	
Baby Blossom	20in (51cm)	Comp/Cloth	composition head, arms, legs, cloth body (looks similar to Effanbee's Bubbles)	1927	Joseph Kallus	$500 – $600
Baby Bo-Kaye	6in (15cm)	All-bisque	fully-jointed	1925	Joseph Kallus	$1800 – $2000
Baby Bo-Kaye	16in (41cm)	Combination	bisque, composition, celluloid heads, cloth body, usually composition arms and legs	1925	Joseph Kallus	$2500
Baby Bo-Kaye	18in (46cm)	Combination	bisque, composition, celluloid heads, cloth body, usually composition arms and legs	1925	Joseph Kallus	$2500 – $2600
Baby Bo-Kaye	20in (51cm)	Combination	bisque, composition, celluloid heads, cloth body, usually composition arms and legs	1925	Joseph Kallus	$2750
Baby Bundie	12in (31cm)	All-composition	jointed arms only, eyes are painted and wig is mohair, Joseph Kallus' first doll	1918	Joseph Kallus	$2800
Baby Bundie	16in (41cm)	All-composition	fully-jointed	1918	Joseph Kallus	

Name	Size	Material Made	Specific Type of Collectible	Year Made	Manufacturer	Current Price
Baby Mine	18in (46cm)	All-vinyl	fully-jointed, painted eyes	1961	Joseph Kallus	$175 – $200
Baby Mine			unusual hinge joints with sleep eyes			***
Baby Snooks	12in (31cm)	Combination	composition head and hands, wood feet, coiled wire body	1939	Ideal	$275 – $300
Bandmaster (Bandy)			advertising figure for General Electric	1935	Joseph Kallus	$850 – $1000
Bank		Glazed Bisque				$300 – $350
Bank		Jasperware	blue and white			$550 – $600
Betty Boop	12in (31cm)	Comp/Wood	composition head, segmented wood arms and legs, molded composition torso	1932	Joseph Kallus	$750 – $800
Bo-Fair				1919	Joseph Kallus	
Bonzo (dog)	12-14in (31-36cm)	All-composition		1928	Joseph Kallus	
Books			The Kewpie Primer	1912	Rose O'Neill	$50 – $100
Books			The Kewpies and Dottie Darling	1910	Rose O'Neill	$125 – $150
Books			The Kewpies and the Runaway Baby	1928	Rose O'Neill	$200 – $300
Books			The Kewpies, Their Book	1912	Rose O'Neill	$150 – $250
Bottle Top		All-bisque	bottle top attached to a cork			$200 – $250
Boutonniere	2.25in (6cm)	All-bisque	attaches through a buttonhole			$150 – $200
Button Hole	2in (5cm)	All-bisque		1913 on	J.D. Kestner	$165 – $175
Bye-Lo Baby		Comp/Cloth	composition head, cloth body	1926	Joseph Kallus	$250
Catalog Sheet		Paper	shows line of Cameo Doll Products		Strombecker Corp.	$25
Champ	16in (41cm)	All-composition	fully-jointed boy doll	1942	Joseph Kallus	$650 – $750
Christmas Tree	3.25in (8cm)	Glass	Christmas tree light of painted glass			$15 – $25
Clock		Jasperware	blue and white, also available in green and pink			$500 – $550
Comic Book			a Will Eisner Production, Spring 1949	1949		$50 – $75
Covered Tall Bowl		Jasperware	blue and white			$400 – $450
Creamers		Glazed Bisque				$75 – $85
Crownie		Comp/Wood body	composition head, segmented wood	1940	Joseph Kallus	
Cups and Saucers		Glazed Bisque				$175 – $225
Dishes		Glazed Bisque	3-piece baby place setting			$500 – $600
Dollie				1921	Joseph Kallus	
Dumbo	8.5in (22cm)	All-composition	elephant with composition, head and trunk jointed, rubber ears, Walt Disney Design	1942	Joseph Kallus	***
Dyp-a-Babe		All-vinyl	all-vinyl and fully-jointed drink and wet feature, packed in a similar layette to the Effanbee Dy-Dee Baby	1956	Joseph Kallus	$150 – $200
Effanbee		Paper	back cover of the 1949 Effanbee doll catalog	1949	Effanbee	
Felix the Cat	3.5in (9cm)	All-wood	segments jointed with elastic	1928	Joseph Kallus	$200 – $225

Name	Size	Material Made	Specific Type of Collectible	Year Made	Manufacturer	Current Price
Felix the Cat	8.5in (22cm)	All-wood	segments jointed with elastic	1928	Joseph Kallus	$300 – $350
Felix the Cat	13in (33cm)	All-wood	segments jointed with elastic	1928	Copyright Pat Sullivan, Joseph Kallus	$450 – $500
Felix the Cat		All-vinyl	fully-jointed	late 1950s	Joseph Kallus	$200 – $250
Finger Bowl		Jasperware	blue and white			$200 – $250
Floppy Kewpie	17in (43cm)	Cloth				***
Floppy Kewpie	21in (53cm)	Cloth				***
Flower Bowl		Jasperware	blue and white			$200 – $250
Giggles	13in (33cm)	All-composition	fully-jointed, molded hair loop for bow	1946	Joseph Kallus	$600 – $650
Greeting Cards		Paper	American Greeting Cards, featuring Rose O'Neill artwork	1973	Joseph Kallus	$3 – $5
Greeting Cards		Paper	large format American Greetings cards, featuring Rose O'Neill artwork	1973	Joseph Kallus	$5 – $10
Hair receiver		Jasperware	blue and white			$400 – $450
Hang Tag			hang tag for Cameo Dolls			$15 – $20
Hatpin Holder		Jasperware	blue and white			$350 – $400
Head	5in (13cm)	All-bisque		1980		$50
Head and Doll	10in (25cm)	All-bisque		1980		$150 – $175
Ho-Ho	3in (8cm)	All-vinyl	good luck doll, laughing voice, 3lbs., item 6053	1965		$20 – $25
Ho-Ho	3in (8cm)	All-vinyl	brown with white painted teeth	1965	Rose O'Neill	$35
Ho-Ho	5in (13cm)	All-vinyl		1965		$35
Ho-Ho	6.25in (16cm)	Plaster	painted in bright colors	1941	Rose O'Neill	$125 – $175
Ho-Ho	7in (18cm)	All-vinyl	good luck doll, laughing voice, 11lbs, item 6057	1965		$60
Ho-Ho			jewelry on a chain			$25
Ho-Ho			soap			$25 – $50
Howdy Doody	13in (33cm)	Comp/Wood	composition head, jointed wood segment body	1947	Noma Electric	$400 – $500
Illustration		Paper	for the cover of The Ladies' Home Journal	1910	Rose O'Neill	$25
Illustration		Paper	for the Woman's Home Companion	1909	Rose O'Neill	$20 – $25
Illustration		Paper	Kewpies catching a culprit selling counterfeit Kewpies		Rose O'Neill	
Illustration		Paper	14 Kewpies hanging on a clothesline		probably drawn by Joseph Kallus	***
Illustration			The Spirit of Kewpies		probably drawn by Joseph Kallus	***
Inkwell		Glazed Bisque				$750 – $1000
Jar		Jasperware	blue and white			$200 – $250
Jeep	9in (23cm)	Comp/Wood	composition and fully-jointed, wood segment tail, licensed by King Features Syndicate	1942	Joseph Kallus	$300 – $400
Jeep	12.5in (32cm)	Comp/Wood	composition and fully-jointed, wood segment tail, licensed by King Features Syndicate	1942	Joseph Kallus	$400 – $450

Name	Size	Material Made	Specific Type of Collectible	Year Made	Manufacturer	Current Price
Jiminy Cricket	9in (23cm)	All-wood	segments, arms and legs are elastic jointed, Walt Disney Designs	1940	Ideal	$450 – $500
Joy			doll similar to Margie with a molded loop on head for a hair ribbon	1932	Joseph Kallus	$350 – $400
Kewpie	1.5in (4cm)	All-bisque	Doodledog, Action Kewpie		J.D. Kestner	$1000 – $1200
Kewpie	2.25in (6cm)	All-bisque	standing dolls with jointed arms, painted eyes glance to either side depending on doll	1913		$100 – $125
Kewpie	2.5in (6cm)	All-bisque	Kewpie in bisque swing, Action Kewpie		J.D. Kestner	$4000
Kewpie	2.5in (6cm)	All-bisque	Kewpie on sled, Action Kewpie		J.D. Kestner	$1000
Kewpie	2.5in (6cm)	All-bisque	jointed arms only	1912+	J.D. Kestner	$125 – $150
Kewpie	2in (5cm)	All-bisque	with rabbit, rose, turkey, pumpkin, shamrock, etc., Action Kewpie		J.D. Kestner	$500 – $550
Kewpie	2in (5cm)	All-bisque	jointed arms only	1912+		$125 – $150
Kewpie	3.25in (8cm)	All-bisque	Kewpie with a surprised look, Action Kewpie			$1000 – $1200
Kewpie	3.5in (9cm)	All-bisque	Guitar player, Action Kewpie		J.D. Kestner	$400 – $500
Kewpie	3.5in (9cm)	All-bisque	Huggers, Action Kewpie		J.D. Kestner	$200 – $225
Kewpie	3.5in (9cm)	All-bisque	Kewpie and Doodledog on bench, Action Kewpie		J.D. Kestner	$4500 – $5000
Kewpie	3.5in (9cm)	All-bisque	Kewpie sitting on inkwell, Action Kewpie		J.D. Kestner	$750 – $1000
Kewpie	3.5in (9cm)	All-bisque	Kewpie Soldiers, sitting, Action Kewpie		J.D. Kestner	$1500
Kewpie	3.5in (9cm)	All-bisque	Kewpie Traveler with Doodledog, Action Kewpie		J.D. Kestner	$1350 – $1650
Kewpie	3.5in (9cm)	All-bisque	Kewpie with bunting babies, Action Kewpie		J.D. Kestner	$4000 – $4500
Kewpie	3.5in (9cm)	All-bisque	Kewpie with cat, Action Kewpie		J.D. Kestner	$650
Kewpie	3.5in (9cm)	All-bisque	Traveler, Action Kewpie		J.D. Kestner	$325 – $350
Kewpie	3.5in (9cm)	All-bisque	Two Kewpies reading book, standing, Action Kewpie		J.D. Kestner	$850 – $950
Kewpie	3.75in (9cm)	All-bisque	Kneeling, with outstretched arms, Action Kewpie		J.D. Kestner	$1100
Kewpie	3-4in (8-10cm)	All-bisque	Reclining or sitting, Action Kewpie		J.D. Kestner	$450 – $500
Kewpie	3in (8cm)	All-bisque	Kewpie holding pen, Action Kewpie		J.D. Kestner	$450 – $500
Kewpie	3in (8cm)	All-bisque	shoulder head	1913 on	J.D. Kestner	$425 – $450
Kewpie	3in (8cm)	All-bisque	Tumbling, Action Kewpie		J.D. Kestner	$650 – $750
Kewpie	4.5in (11cm)	All-bisque	Kewpie at tea table, Action Kewpie		J.D. Kestner	$3250 – $3500
Kewpie	4.5in (11cm)	All-bisque	Kewpie riding animal		J.D. Kestner	$5000 – $5500
Kewpie	4.5in (11cm)	All-bisque	Kewpie riding hobby horse		J.D. Kestner	$5500
Kewpie	4.5in (11cm)	All-bisque	molded dress and hat	1913 on	J.D. Kestner	$1800
Kewpie	4.5in (12cm)	All-bisque	black Kewpie with jointed arms, chocolate color with blue painted wings			$200 – $250
Kewpie	4.75in (12cm)	All-bisque	Thumb Sucker, smoothly finished	1973	Lefton	$75 – $100
Kewpie	4in (10cm)	All-bisque	Crawling, Action Kewpie		J.D. Kestner	$900

Name	Size	Material Made	Specific Type of Collectible	Year Made	Manufacturer	Current Price
Kewpie	4in (10cm)	All-bisque	Farmer, Fireman (molded hats), Action Kewpie		J.D. Kestner	$1000
Kewpie	4in (10cm)	All-bisque	Governor or Mayor, Action Kewpie		J.D. Kestner	$500 – $750
Kewpie	4in (10cm)	All-bisque	jointed hips	1913 on	J.D. Kestner	$500 – $550
Kewpie	4in (10cm)	All-bisque	Kewpie Bellhop in green, Action Kewpie		J.D. Kestner	$1750 – $1800
Kewpie	4in (10cm)	All-bisque	Kewpie holding teddy bear, Action Kewpie		J.D. Kestner	$800 – $950
Kewpie	4in (10cm)	All-bisque	Kewpie with basket, Action Kewpie		J.D. Kestner	$1000 – $1200
Kewpie	4in (10cm)	All-bisque	Thinker, Action Kewpie		J.D. Kestner	$275 – $325
Kewpie	4in (10cm)	All-bisque	jointed arms and legs	1912+		$550 – $600
Kewpie	4in (10cm)	All-bisque	jointed arms only	1912+	J.D. Kestner	$150
Kewpie	5.5in (13cm)	All-bisque	Two Kewpies reading book, Action Kewpie		J.D. Kestner	$2200
Kewpie	5.5in (14cm)	All-bisque	Kewpie in blue felt hat, Action Kewpie		J.D. Kestner	$3800
Kewpie	5.5in (14cm)	All-bisque	Thinker, incised O'Neill			
Kewpie	5-6in (13-15cm)	All-bisque	Kewpie Soldiers, standing, Action Kewpie		J.D. Kestner	$950 – $1250
Kewpie	5in (10cm)	All-bisque	Kewpie with broom & dustpan		J.D. Kestner	$850
Kewpie	5in (13cm)	All-bisque	only the arms are jointed and each is incised with O'Neill on the bottom			$225 – $250
Kewpie	5in (13cm)	All-bisque	Black Hottentot	1913 on	J.D. Kestner	$650 – $750
Kewpie	5in (13cm)	All-bisque	painted shoes and socks	1913 on	J.D. Kestner	$600 – $700
Kewpie	5in (13cm)	All-bisque	standing dolls with jointed arms, painted eyes glance to either side depending on doll	1913		
Kewpie	5in (13cm)	All-bisque	jointed arms only	1912+	J.D. Kestner	$185
Kewpie	6.25in (16cm)	All-bisque	only the arms are jointed and each is incised with O'Neill on the bottom			$250 – $300
Kewpie	6in (15cm)	All-bisque	jointed arms and legs			$850+
Kewpie	6in (15cm)	All-bisque	jointed hips	1913 on	J.D. Kestner	$850
Kewpie	6in (15cm)	All-bisque	standing dolls with jointed arms, painted eyes glance to either side depending on doll	1913		$250 – $300
Kewpie	6in (15cm)	All-bisque	glass eyes and wig	1913 on	J.D. Kestner	$2500 – $3500
Kewpie	6in (15cm)	All-bisque	jointed arms only	1912+	J.D. Kestner	$250
Kewpie	7.5in (19cm)	All-bisque	jointed arms only	1912+		$300 – $350
Kewpie	7in (18cm)	All-bisque	Thinker, Action Kewpie		J.D. Kestner	$500 – $550
Kewpie	7in (18cm)	All-bisque	jointed arms only	1912+	J.D. Kestner	$300 – $350
Kewpie	8in (20cm)	All-bisque	jointed hips	1913 on	J.D. Kestner	$1250
Kewpie	8in (20cm)	All-bisque	jointed arms only	1912+	J.D. Kestner	$400 – $500
Kewpie	9in (23cm)	All-bisque	jointed arms only	1912+	J.D. Kestner	$600 – $700
Kewpie	10.5in (27cm)	All-bisque	jointed arms only	1912+		$1000 – $1200
Kewpie	10in (25cm)	All-bisque	only the arms are jointed and each is incised with O'Neill on the bottom	1913 on	J.D. Kestner	$800
Kewpie	11in (28cm)	All-bisque	painted shoes and socks	1913 on	J.D. Kestner	$1500 – $1800

Name	Size	Material Made	Specific Type of Collectible	Year Made	Manufacturer	Current Price
Kewpie	11in (28cm)	All-bisque	jointed arms only	1912+		$1200 – $1300
Kewpie	12in (31cm)	All-bisque	standing dolls with jointed arms, painted eyes glance to either side depending on doll	1913	J.D. Kestner	$1500 – $1600
Kewpie	12in (31cm)	All-bisque	jointed arms only	1912+	J.D. Kestner	$1500 – $1600
Kewpie	n/a	All-bisque	Kewpie Mountain with 17 figures, Action Kewpie		J.D. Kestner	$50,000 – $75,000
Kewpie	2.25in (6cm)	All-celluloid	Black Hottentot, with jointed arms			$125 – $150
Kewpie	2.25in (6cm)	All-celluloid	most have jointed arms	1915+		$50 – $60
Kewpie	2.5in (6cm)	All-celluloid	Black Hottentot, with jointed arms		Karl Standfuss	$125 – $150
Kewpie	2.5in (6cm)	All-celluloid	Kewpie-Billikin combination of celluloid with no markings, jointed arms serve both sides	1915+		$150 – $175
Kewpie	2.5in (6cm)	All-celluloid	most have jointed arms	1915+	Karl Standfuss	$50 – $60
Kewpie	22in (56cm)	All-celluloid	most have jointed arms	1915+	Karl Standfuss	$650 – $750
Kewpie	2in (5cm)	All-celluloid	most have jointed arms	1915+		$40 – $50
Kewpie	3.25in (8cm)	All-celluloid	bride and groom, celluloid with jointed arms			$150 pair
Kewpie	3.25in (8cm)	All-celluloid	most have jointed arms	1915+		$50 – $60
Kewpie	3.5in (9cm)	All-celluloid	Huggers, no jointed parts, 2 Kewpies arms wrapped around each other	1915+		$60 – $75
Kewpie	3.5in (9cm)	All-celluloid	most have jointed arms	1915+		$65 – $75
Kewpie	3in (8cm)	All-celluloid	also in other sizes, Bride and Groom for a wedding cake decoration	1915+		$150 pair
Kewpie	3in (8cm)	All-celluloid	most have jointed arms	1915+		$50 – $60
Kewpie	3in (8cm)	All-celluloid	Instructor, no jointed parts	1915+		$75 – $100
Kewpie	3in (8cm)	All-celluloid	with a rabbit, no jointed parts	1915+		$100 – $110
Kewpie	4.5in (12cm)	All-celluloid	most have jointed arms	1915+		$100 – $125
Kewpie	4in (10cm)	All-celluloid	jointed arms, two-in-one doll, Kewpie on one side, Billikin on the other	1915+		$200 – $225
Kewpie	4in (10cm)	All-celluloid	most have jointed arms	1915+		$100 – $125
Kewpie	5.25in (13cm)	All-celluloid	most have jointed arms	1915+		$125 – $150
Kewpie	5in (13cm)	All-celluloid	Black Hottentot		Karl Standfuss	$200 – $250
Kewpie	5in (13cm)	All-celluloid	most have jointed arms	1915+		$125 – $150
Kewpie	5in (13cm)	All-celluloid	with a painted bathing suit and hat	1915+		$125 – $150
Kewpie	5in (13cm)	All-celluloid	most have jointed arms		Karl Standfuss	$125 – $150
Kewpie	6.5in (17cm)	All-celluloid	most have jointed arms	1915+		$150
Kewpie	7.5in (19cm)	All-celluloid	most have jointed arms	1915+		$150 – $175
Kewpie	7in (18cm)	All-celluloid	Black Hottentot, with jointed arms, with wings			$225
Kewpie	7in (18cm)	All-celluloid	most have jointed arms	1915+		$125 – $150
Kewpie	8.5in (22cm)	All-celluloid	jointed arms			$150 – $175
Kewpie	8in (20cm)	All-celluloid	most have jointed arms		Karl Standfuss	$200 – $225

Name	Size	Material Made	Specific Type of Collectible	Year Made	Manufacturer	Current Price
Kewpie	9in (23cm)	All-celluloid	jointed arms, black version with no topknot		King Innovations, Inc.	$225 – $250
Kewpie	10in (25cm)	All-celluloid	most have jointed arms	1915+		$250+
Kewpie	11.25in (29cm)	All-celluloid	most have jointed arms	1915+		$300+
Kewpie	12in (31cm)	All-celluloid			Karl Standfuss	$350 – $400
Kewpie	14.5in (37cm)	All-celluloid	jointed arms only			$250 – $300
Kewpie	8in (20cm)	All-cloth	mask face and a jersey body in red, blue, green, coral, yellow or pink	1926+	Richard G. Kreuger	$200 – $225
Kewpie	9in (23cm)	All-cloth	mask face and a plush body	1926+	King Innovations, Inc.	$225 – $250
Kewpie	11in (28cm)	All-cloth	mask face and a jersey body in red, blue, green, coral, yellow or pink	1926+	Richard G. Kreuger	$225 – $250
Kewpie	11in (28cm)	All-cloth	painted mask faces	1930s	King Innovations, Inc.	$225 – $250
Kewpie	11in (28cm)	All-cloth	wearing dresses	1926+	King Innovations, Inc.	$225 – $250
Kewpie	12in (31cm)	All-cloth	bunny ears on the head, jersey body is pink		King Innovations, Inc.	$250 – $300
Kewpie	12in (31cm)	All-cloth	mask face and a plush body	1926+	King Innovations, Inc.	$250 – $300
Kewpie	14in (36cm)	All-cloth	mask face and a jersey body in red, blue, green, coral, yellow or pink	1926+	Richard G. Kreuger	$300 – $325
Kewpie	15in (38cm)	All-cloth	mask face and a plush body	1926+	King Innovations, Inc.	$325 – $350
Kewpie	17in (43cm)	All-cloth	mask face and a jersey body in red, blue, green, coral, yellow or pink	1926+	Richard G. Kreuger	$400 – $450
Kewpie	18in (46cm)	All-cloth	mask face and a plush body	1926+	King Innovations, Inc.	$450 – $500
Kewpie	21in (53cm)	All-cloth	mask face and a jersey body in red, blue, green, coral, yellow or pink	1926+	Richard G. Kreuger	$500 – $550
Kewpie	22in (56cm)	All-cloth	mask face and a plush body	1926+	King Innovations, Inc.	$550 – $600
Kewpie	7in (18cm)	All-composition	talcum container with painted features			$200 – $225
Kewpie	7in (18cm)	All-composition	jointed arms only			$150 – $175
Kewpie	7in (18cm)	All-composition	jointed arms, usually attached to a base or "pedestal" can have mohair wigs over molded Kewpie hair	1916+		$175 – $200
Kewpie	8in (20cm)	All-composition	jointed at shoulders, some at hips; good condition	1916+	Cameo Doll Co., Rex Doll Co., and Mutual Doll Co.	$200 – $250
Kewpie	8in (20cm)	All-composition	jointed arms, usually attached to a base or "pedestal" can have mohair wigs over molded Kewpie hair	1916+		$200 – $225
Kewpie	10in (25cm)	All-composition	jointed arms, usually attached to a base or "pedestal" can have mohair wigs over molded Kewpie hair	1916+		$150 – $200
Kewpie	11.5in (29cm)	All-composition	jointed arms, free-standing with legs apart, also as black dolls (1940s)	1916+		$275 – $325
Kewpie	11.5in (29cm)	All-composition	jointed arms, usually attached to a base or "pedestal" can have mohair wigs over molded Kewpie hair	1916+		$200 – $300
Kewpie	12in (31cm)	All-composition	fully-jointed	1916+		$250 – $300
Kewpie	12in (31cm)	All-composition	jointed arms, usually attached to a base or "pedestal" can have mohair wigs over molded Kewpie hair	1916+		$200 – $300

Name	Size	Material Made	Specific Type of Collectible	Year Made	Manufacturer	Current Price
Kewpie	12.5in (32cm)	All-composition	attached to a blue pedestal, jointed arms	before 1920		$200 – $300
Kewpie	13in (33cm)	All-composition	fully-jointed	1916+		$300 – $350
Kewpie	13in (33cm)	All-composition	fully-jointed	1940s	Cameo, dist. By Noma Electric (Effanbee)	$300 – $350
Kewpie	15in (38cm)	All-composition	fully-jointed	1916+		$350 – $400
Kewpie		All-composition	all original, boxed, jointed at shoulders, some at hips; good condition		Cameo Doll Co., Rex Doll Co., and Mutual Doll Co.	$550 – $600
Kewpie		All-composition	in sunsuit, fully-jointed			$250 – $300
Kewpie	6in (15cm)	All-hard plastic	jointed arms, part of a "Kewpie Kard"	1986	Jesco, Inc.	$15 – $20
Kewpie	8in (20cm)	All-hard plastic	standing Kewpie, 1-piece with jointed arms	1950s		$150 – $165
Kewpie	9in (23cm)	All-hard plastic	jointed arms only	1950s	Rose O'Neill	$100 – $150
Kewpie	13in (33cm)	All-hard plastic	fully-jointed with sleep eyes, all original clothes	1950s		$500
Kewpie	13.5in (34cm)	All-hard plastic	fully-jointed with sleep eyes from Effanbee	1949+	Effanbee	$400 – $500
Kewpie	4in (10cm)	All-vinyl	Thinker	1952+		$15 – $20
Kewpie	4.25in (11cm)	All-vinyl	jointed head only	1952+		$35 – $40
Kewpie	6in (15cm)	All-vinyl	jointed head only	1952+		$15 – $20
Kewpie	6in (15cm)	All-vinyl		early 1970s		$15 – $20
Kewpie	8in (20cm)	All-vinyl	fully-jointed	1952+		$50
Kewpie	8in (20cm)	All-vinyl	fully-jointed, dressed in original old-fashioned costume to celebrate Kewpie's 60th birthday	1973	Amsco	$20 – $25
Kewpie	9.5in (24cm)	All-vinyl	Twins, jointed head only, stationary glassine eyes are stationary		Cameo	$250 – $300 pair
Kewpie	9.5in (24cm)	All-vinyl	inset plastic eyes	1952+		$50 – $75
Kewpie	10in (25cm)	All-vinyl		early 1970s		
Kewpie	11in (28cm)	All-vinyl	jointed head only	1952+		$25 – $50
Kewpie	12in (31cm)	All-vinyl	fully-jointed	1973	Amsco	$50 – $60
Kewpie	12in (31cm)	All-vinyl	fully-jointed	1952+		$100+
Kewpie	12in (31cm)	All-vinyl		1952+	Jesco, Inc.	$50 – $75
Kewpie	12in (31cm)	All-vinyl		1983	Jesco, Inc.	$50 – $75
Kewpie	12-13in (31-33cm)	All-vinyl	all original and excellent condition	1960s	Cameo Doll Co.	$100 – $110
Kewpie	13in (33cm)	All-vinyl	rooted hair	1952+		$200 – $300
Kewpie	13.5in (34cm)	All-vinyl	vinyl head and arms, blow mold body and legs (thin plastic)	1952+		
Kewpie	14in (36cm)	All-vinyl	fully-jointed	1952+		$75 – $85
Kewpie	14in (36cm)	All-vinyl		early 1970s		$65 – $75
Kewpie	16in (41cm)	All-vinyl	all original and excellent condition	1960s	Cameo Doll Co.	$135 – $165
Kewpie	16in (41cm)	All-vinyl	fully-jointed	1952+		$135 – $165
Kewpie	16in (41cm)	All-vinyl	Kewpie Baby with hinged body	1960s	Cameo Doll Co.	$250
Kewpie	16in (41cm)	All-vinyl		1983	Jesco, Inc.	$75 – $95

Name	Size	Material Made	Specific Type of Collectible	Year Made	Manufacturer	Current Price
Kewpie	18in (46cm)	All-vinyl		1952+	Jesco, Inc.	$85 – $100
Kewpie	19.5in (50cm)	All-vinyl	vinyl head and arms, blow mold body and legs (thin plastic)	1952+		
Kewpie	21in (53cm)	All-vinyl	rooted hair and Miss Peeps body	1952+	Joseph Kallus	$500 – $700
Kewpie	26.5in (67cm)	All-vinyl	girl in dress	1952+	Jesco, Inc.	$175 – $200
Kewpie	26.5in (67cm)	All-vinyl	sailor	1983	Jesco	$200 – $225
Kewpie	27in (69cm)	All-vinyl		early 1970s	Strombecker	$200
Kewpie	27in (69cm)	All-vinyl	fully-jointed	1952+		$250
Kewpie		All-vinyl	Kewpie with a vinyl Felix the Cat	1950s		$125 – $150
Kewpie		All-vinyl	fully-jointed and shoes are prototypes			$125 – $150
Kewpie	6in (15cm)	Bisque/Cloth	painted eyes; bisque shoulder head, arms, legs with cloth body	1912+		
Kewpie	10in (25cm)	Bisque/Comp	glass eyes, bisque head on chubby jointed composition toddler body, 5 piece body		J.D. Kestner	$5000
Kewpie	12in (31cm)	Bisque/Cloth	painted eyes; bisque shoulder head, arms, legs with cloth body	1912+		
Kewpie	12in (31cm)	Bisque/Cloth	glass eyes, bisque head on cloth body		Alt, Beck & Gottschalck	$3000 – $3200
Kewpie	12in (31cm)	Bisque/Cloth	painted eyes, bisque head on cloth body		Alt, Beck & Gottschalck	$2000 – $2500
Kewpie	12-14in (31-36cm)	Bisque/Comp	glass eyes, bisque head on chubby jointed composition toddler body, 5 piece body		J.D. Kestner	$6500 – $7500
Kewpie	13.5in (34cm)	Bisque/Comp	round glass eyes, bisque head, flange neck, cloth body or composition body	1912+		$7500 – $8000
Kewpie	12in (31cm)	Comp/Cloth	composition head, cloth body, jointed at shoulders, some at hips; good condition	1916+	Cameo Doll Co., Rex Doll Co., and Mutual Doll Co.	$250 – $275
Kewpie	12in (31cm)	Comp/Cloth	composition heads and cloth bodies, composition lower arms	before 1940s		$200 – $250
Kewpie	23in (58cm)	Comp/Cloth	composition head, cloth body	1916+		$2500 – $3000
Kewpie	23in (58cm)	Comp/Cloth	composition heads and cloth bodies	before 1940s		$2500 – $3000
Kewpie		Glazed Bisque	Kewpie lying on a box with a lid			$850 – $950
Kewpie	33in (84cm)	Paper-mache	paper-mache used for an advertising piece	before 1920		$500 – $750
Kewpie	3-6in (8-15cm)	Porcelain	Thinker (One of the most common forms of Kewpie in all media)			$200 – $225
Kewpie	4in (10cm)	Washable Vinyl	Sitting Kewpie, in "Thinker Pose", with cooing voice, 2lbs., item 6004		Cameo Doll Co.	$10 – $12
Kewpie	6in (15cm)	Washable Vinyl	Sleeper, 3lbs., item 6116		Cameo Doll Co.	$15 – $20
Kewpie	11in (28cm)	Washable Vinyl	Sleeper, 7lbs., item 6181, white version		Cameo Doll Co.	$50 – $60
Kewpie	11in (28cm)	Washable Vinyl	Sleeper, head is jointed, item 6191, black version		Cameo Doll Co.	$65 – $75
Kewpie	2in (5cm)		holdng a double gold wedding ring, Action Kewpie			$500 – $650
Kewpie	2in (5cm)		Kewpie with a peep (or chicken) coming out of an egg			$425 – $450

Name	Size	Material Made	Specific Type of Collectible	Year Made	Manufacturer	Current Price
Kewpie	2.5in (6cm)		Governor, sitting in a wicker chair			$175 – $225
Kewpie	2.5in (6cm)		place card holder that hangs on a cup			$350 – $450
Kewpie	2.75in (7cm)		Lying soldier			$350 – $450
Kewpie	2-5in (5-13cm)		Traveler (carrys an umbrella and a suitcase)			$250 – $500
Kewpie	3.25in (8cm)			1973	Lefton	$35 – $50
Kewpie	3.5in (9cm)			1973	Lefton	$35 – $50
Kewpie	3.5in (9cm)		Traveler with a black umbrella and a brown suitcase			$325 – $350
Kewpie	4in (10cm)		Huggers - two Kewpies with arms wrapped around each other			$250 – $350
Kewpie	4in (10cm)		Policeman		Amsco	$1000
Kewpie	4in (10cm)		Thinker, called Kewpie Love	1975	Amsco	$5 – $15
Kewpie	4in (10cm)		made in Japan, KW913 stamped on the back	1973	Lefton	$35 – $50
Kewpie	4in (10cm)		Sweet Serenade, Item no. 5160	1985	Extra Special, Inc.	$50 – $75
Kewpie	4in (10cm)		Indian Kewpie, marked Rose O'Neill	1970s		$50 – $75
Kewpie	4.25in (11cm)		Kewpie holding a Kewpie holding a Kewpie			$150+
Kewpie	4.5in (12cm)		Kewpie vase, w/Kewpie in a birthday hat that has a blue flower in it, whistle is bright pink, vase is white			***
Kewpie	5in (13cm)		Huggers - two Kewpies with arms wrapped around each other			$300 – $350
Kewpie	5.5in (14cm)		wearing a dress and holding a cup decorated with gold trim			$125 – $150
Kewpie	6in (15cm)		jointed head	1975	Amsco	$5 – $10
Kewpie	8in (20cm)		fully-jointed	1975	Amsco	$15 – $20
Kewpie	8in (20cm)		Black Hottentot, boxed	1980s	Jesco	$40 – $45
Kewpie	11in (28cm)		jointed head	1975	Amsco, Joseph Kallus	$10 – $20
Kewpie	11.5in (29cm)		jointed arms only	late 1940s	Rose O'Neill	
Kewpie	12in (31cm)		fully-jointed	1975	Amsco	$25 – $50
Kewpie	12in (31cm)		boxed	1980s	Jesco, Inc.	$60
Kewpie	13in (33cm)		fully-jointed Noma Electric (Effanbee) in a sunsuit	late 1940s		$350+
Kewpie	15in (38cm)		fully-jointed	1975	Amsco	
Kewpie	18in (46cm)		boxed	1980s	Jesco, Inc.	$85
Kewpie	24in (61cm)		boxed	1980s	Jesco, Inc.	$200 – $250
Kewpie	27in (69cm)		fully-jointed, largest Kewpie ever made	1975	Amsco	$100 – $125
Kewpie			baby with bottle, Action Kewpie			$3500+
Kewpie			with hands in the air, Action Kewpie			$1250 – $1500
Kewpie			lying on back with feet in the air, Action Kewpie			$350 – $550
Kewpie			lying on stomach, Action Kewpie			$350 – $550

Name	Size	Material Made	Specific Type of Collectible	Year Made	Manufacturer	Current Price
Kewpie			one Kewpie feeding the other with a spoon from a porridge bowl, Action Kewpie			$3000 – $4000
Kewpie			peering out of a basket of flowers, Action Kewpie			$1750+
Kewpie			polishing boot, Action Kewpie			$1800 – $2000
Kewpie			seated and kicking out left leg, Action Kewpie			$600+
Kewpie			seated and kicking out right leg, Action Kewpie			$600+
Kewpie			wearing boots, Action Kewpie			$600+
Kewpie			with molded clothing, Action Kewpie			$1800 – $2500
Kewpie			Aviator (with molded binoculars)			$2000+
Kewpie			Bather (with sand pail)			$1000 – $1250
Kewpie			Bookworm (seated with book on lap)			$850+
Kewpie			Boxer (a variation of the Huggers, but much rarer)			$4000 – $4500
Kewpie			Farmer			$1000+
Kewpie			Gardner			$1000+
Kewpie			Golfer			$2000 – $2500
Kewpie			Lawyer			$550 – $650
Kewpie			Mother and child (with large baby bottle)			$4500+
Kewpie			Musician with a drum			$2500+
Kewpie			Musician with a mandolin			$400 – $500
Kewpie			Sailor			$1000+
Kewpie			Soldier - Confederate soldier			$400 – $500
Kewpie			Soldier - German soldier coming out of an egg shell (very rare)			$5000+
Kewpie			Soldier - soldier wearing a "Rough Rider" hat			$2000 – $2500
Kewpie			Soldier - soldier wearing a Prussian helmet and dressed as a Prussian soldier			$2000 – $3000
Kewpie			Soldier - wearing a plumed helmat (very rare)			$3500+
Kewpie			Soldier - wounded soldier			$3500+
Kewpie			Student (wearing glasses and reading a book)			$1800+
Kewpie			Sweeper (with a broom)			$250 – $450
Kewpie			with an object, holding a heart			***
Kewpie			with an object, holding a rose			$200 – $250
Kewpie			with an object, holding a rose and seated in a hammock			$3800 – $4200
Kewpie			with an object, holding a sack			$1200 – $1500
Kewpie			with an object, in a swing			$3200 – $3500

Name	Size	Material Made	Specific Type of Collectible	Year Made	Manufacturer	Current Price
Kewpie			with an object, in bed			$4000+
Kewpie			with an object, seated in a sea shell			$4000+
Kewpie			with an object, standing on a sea shell			$4000+
Kewpie			with an object, with a cup			***
Kewpie			with an object, with a hat and purse (attached to vase)			***
Kewpie			with an object, with comb seated in bathtub			$3000+
Kewpie			with an object, with flowers attached to a vase			$2000+
Kewpie			with an object, with outhouse			***
Kewpie			with an object, with potted plant			$250+
Kewpie			with an object, with yoke and buckets on a chain			$3500 – $4000
Kewpie			with animal, bee on foot			$600+
Kewpie			with animal, butterfly in hand			$950 – $1000
Kewpie			with animal, fly on Kewpie's toe			$950+
Kewpie			with animal, riding a goose			$5000+
Kewpie			with animal, with a chicken			$250 – $350
Kewpie			with animal, with a chicken and a vase full of eggs			***
Kewpie			with animal, elephant is on his back; Kewpie is seated on his stomach			$4500 – $5000
Kewpie			with animal, elephant is sitting by Kewpie			$3500 – $4000
Kewpie			with animal, with Kewpie Doodle Dog, Kewpie and Doodle Dog on a bench			$4500 – $5000
Kewpie			with animal, with Kewpie Doodle Dog, Kewpie and Doodle Dog on a bench; dog is being fed from a bottle			$5500+
Kewpie			with animal, with Kewpie Doodle Dog, Kewpie and Doodle Dog on a log			$5500+
Kewpie			with animal, with Kewpie Doodle Dog, Kewpie and Doodle Dog with an umbrella			$2250 – $2500
Kewpie			with animal, with Kewpie Doodle Dog, Kewpie lying on his stomach; dog is on his back			$3000 – $3500
Kewpie			with animal, with Kewpie Doodle Dog, Kewpie seated on Doodle Dog			$3500 – $4000
Kewpie			with animal, with two cats; one is black and one is gray			$1500 – $2000
Kewpie			With curly rooted hair			$300 – $400
Kewpie Doodle Dog	3in (8cm)	All-bisque	Action Kewpie		J.D. Kestner	$2500
Kewpie Doodle Dog	4.5in (11cm)	All-bisque	Action Kewpie		J.D. Kestner	$3200 – $3500
Kewpie Doodle Dog	2.5in (6cm)	Glazed China	a copy of the current product made in Japan		Shackman	$5 – $8

Name	Size	Material Made	Specific Type of Collectible	Year Made	Manufacturer	Current Price
Kewpie Doddle Dog	1.5in (4cm)		Alone			$1000+
Kewpie Doddle Dog	3in (8cm)		Alone			$2500+
Kewpie Doddle Dog	5in (13cm)		Alone			$4000+
Kewpie Doddle Dog			attached to an olive green bisque box			$4000+
Kewpie Doddle Dog			molded to a bath tub			$4000 – $4500
Kewpie Doddle Dog			with a sun flower			$4500 – $5000+
Kewpie Gal	8in (20cm)	All-vinyl		1960s	Cameo Doll Co.	$75 – $85
Kewpie Gal	8.5in (22cm)	All-vinyl	fully-jointed, painted brown hair and inserted blue velvet ribbon, no shoes	1969-1973	Strombecker	$25 – $35
Kewpie Gal	8.5in (22cm)	All-vinyl	molded hair with an inset cloth ribbon	1952+		$75 – $85
Kewpie Gal	12in (31cm)	All-vinyl	fully-jointed, molded hair with an inset cloth ribbon, fits into slits on either side of head	1952+	Amsco	$50
Kewpie Gal	14in (36cm)	All-vinyl		1960s	Cameo Doll Co.	$125 – $150
Kewpie Gal	12in (31cm)			1975	Amsco, Joseph Kallus	$50 – $75
Klothespin Box		Jasperware	blue and white			$450 – $550
Kuddly Kewpie	7in (18cm)	All-cloth	bodies are a combination of plush and cloth, some have bunny ears	1952+		$50 – $75
Kuddly Kewpie	9in (23cm)	All-cloth	bodies are a combination of plush and cloth, some have bunny ears	1952+		$50 – $75
Kuddly Kewpie	9in (23cm)	Vinyl/Cloth	with vinyl face and cloth and plush body portions, in seated position		Knickerbocker Toy Co.	$50 – $100
Kuddly Kewpie	8in (20cm)	Washable Vinyl	moveable arms, legs and head, top knot and cooing voice, 9lbs., item 6208		Cameo Doll Co.	$25 – $35
Kuddly Kewpie	12in (31cm)	Washable Vinyl	moveable arms, legs and head, top knot and cooing voice, 13lbs., item 6212		Cameo Doll Co.	$75
Little Annie Rooney (Roonie)	13.5in (34cm)	All-composition	fully-jointed from Jack Collins cartoon	1926	Joseph Kallus	$650
Little Annie Rooney (Roonie)	16in (41cm)	All-composition	fully-jointed from Jack Collins cartoon	1926	Joseph Kallus	$750
Marcia		All-composition	girl with painted features and molded hair	1933	Joseph Kallus	
Margie	17in (43cm)	All-vinyl	fully-jointed, sleep eyes and rooted hair	1958	Cameo Doll Co.	$175 – $225
Margie	17in (43cm)	All-vinyl	fully-jointed, sleep eyes and rooted hair	1958	Joseph Kallus	$175 – $225
Margie	5in (13cm)	Comp/Wood	composition head, segmented wood body	1929	Joseph Kallus	
Margie	9.5in (24cm)	Comp/Wood	composition head, segmented wood body	1929	Joseph Kallus	$200 – $300
Margie		Comp/Wood	composition head with painted features and molded hair, segmented wood body	1929		$500 – $600
Miss Peep	16in (41cm)	All-vinyl	fully-jointed with hinge joints, painted eyes and hair	1969	Joseph Kallus	$125

Name	Size	Material Made	Specific Type of Collectible	Year Made	Manufacturer	Current Price
Miss Peep	18.5in (47cm)	All-vinyl	fully-jointed with hinge joints, painted eyes and hair	1969	Joseph Kallus	$135
Miss Peep	20in (51cm)	All-vinyl	fully-jointed with hinge joints, painted eyes and hair	1969	Joseph Kallus	$150
Miss Peep	16in (41cm)	Washable Vinyl	coos and cries, exclusive "life movement joints", 20lbs., item 6818		Cameo Doll Co.	$75 – $85
Miss Peep	18in	Washable Vinyl	coos and cries, exclusive "life movement joints", 20lbs., item 6818		Cameo Doll Co.	$100 – $125
Mr. Peanut		Comp/Wood	composition and wood segments	1935	Joseph Kallus	$275 – $375
Noma Electric		Paper	late 1940s toy catalog showing the two styles of all composition Kewpies from that time	late 1940s	Noma Electric	
Peanut	18.5in (47cm)	All-vinyl	fully-jointed, drink and wet feature, extra joints at the wristsv	1958	Joseph Kallus	$150 – $200
Perfume Bottle	4.5in (11cm)	All-bisque		1913 on	J.D. Kestner	$550 – $600
Perfume Bottles		Glazed Bisque				$950 – $1250
Pete the Pup	10.5in (27cm)	Comp/Wood	composition head, jointed wood segment body	1942	Joseph Kallus	$350 – $400
Pincushion	2-3in (5-8cm)	All-bisque		1913 on	J.D. Kestner	$250 – $300
Pinkie	27in (69cm)	All-vinyl	fully-jointed with rooted hair	1950s	Joseph Kallus	
Pinkie			similar to Margie with a baby head	1930	Joseph Kallus	$250 – $300
Pinocchio	8in (20cm)	Comp/Wood	composition head, segmented body, Walt Disney Designs	1940	Ideal	$350 – $450
Pinocchio	11in (28cm)	Comp/Wood	composition head, segmented body, Walt Disney Designs	1940	Ideal	$450 – $500
Pinocchio	20in (51cm)	Comp/Wood	composition head, segmented body, Walt Disney Designs	1940	Ideal	$800 – $900
Pitcher		Glazed Bisque				$375 – $475
Pitcher		Jasperware	blue and white, also available in green and pink			$200 – $250
Place Card		All-bisque	Place card that is a Soldier shooting a bug			$550 – $600
Place Cards	2in (5cm)	All-bisque	place cards that are 2in Kewpies attached to a bisque holder: Blunderboo			$450
Place Cards	2in (5cm)	All-bisque	place cards that are 2in Kewpies attached to a bisque holder: Holding a Rose			$450
Place Cards	2in (5cm)	All-bisque	place cards that are 2in Kewpies attached to a bisque holder: Mandolin Player			$500
Place Cards	2in (5cm)	All-bisque	place cards that are 2in Kewpies attached to a bisque holder: Reader			$500
Planter		Glazed Bisque	planter, with the Thinker (pink, white and blue)			$20 – $50
Plaques		Jasperware	blue and white, also available in green and pink	1973	American Greetings	$25
Plate		Glazed Bisque	Child's Bavarian plate			$175 – $225
Popeye		All-vinyl	fully-jointed	1957-1959	Joseph Kallus	$200 – $225
Popeye	14.5in (37cm)	Comp/Wood	composition head, jointed wood segment body, licensed by King Features Syndicate	1942	Joseph Kallus	$350 – $400

Name	Size	Material Made	Specific Type of Collectible	Year Made	Manufacturer	Current Price
Ragsy Kewpie	8in (20cm)	All-vinyl	jointed head, one-piece body	1952+		$40 – $45
Ragsy Kewpie	8in (20cm)	All-vinyl	molded clothes	1960s	Cameo Doll Co.	$40 – $45
Ragsy Kewpie	8in (20cm)	All-vinyl		1975	Amsco	$10 – $15
Ragsy Kewpie	8in (20cm)	Washable Vinyl	in red and blue, coos and cries, 10lbs, item 6108		Cameo Doll Co.	$20 – $25
Ragsy Kewpie			wearing a sunsuit		Joseph Kallus	***
RCA Radiotron	15.5in (39cm)		also called The Selling Fool, composition head with a hat that is a radio tube, body segmented wood	1930	Joseph Kallus	$800 – $900
Rose O'Neill	15.5in (39cm)		Rose O'Neill doll from the 1982 UFDC convention souvenir doll	1982	Lita Wilson and Muriel Kramer	$150 – $175
Scootles	12in (31cm)	All original		1980s	Cameo Doll Co.	$40 – $60
Scootles	14in (36cm)	All original		1964	Cameo Doll Co.	$175 – $200
Scootles	16in (41cm)	All original	Ltd. Ed. Maxines	1973	Cameo Doll Co.	$200 – $225
Scootles	4.5in (12cm)	All-bisque	jointed arms, painted features and hair			$250
Scootles	5-6in (13-15cm)	All-bisque	jointed only at arms	1929+		$400 – $450
Scootles	5-6in (13-15cm)	All-bisque	marked on feet		Cameo Doll Co.	$650 – $750
Scootles	6-7in (15-18cm)	All-bisque	marked on feet		Cameo Doll Co.	$500 – $550
Scootles	18.5in (47cm)	All-cloth	painted blue eyes and a yarn wig			$700 – $750
Scootles	7-8in (18-20cm)	All-composition	appropriate clothes; all in very good condition	1925	Cameo Doll Co., Rose O'Neill	$500 – $600
Scootles	8in (20cm)	All-composition	fully-jointed	1930s		$500 – $600
Scootles	8in (20cm)	All-composition	fully-jointed with painted eyes and hair, no marks			$500 – $600
Scootles	8in (20cm)	All-composition	jointed arms, legs and head; painted eyes or sleep eyes; painted hair	1929+	Cameo Doll Co.	$650 – $750
Scootles	9.5in (24cm)	All-composition	jointed arms, legs and head; painted eyes or sleep eyes; painted hair	1929+	Cameo Doll Co.	$650 – $750
Scootles	12in (31cm)	All-composition		1930s		$450 – $500
Scootles	12in (31cm)	All-composition	sleep eyes		Cameo Doll Co.	$700 – $750
Scootles	12.5in (32cm)	All-composition	fully-jointed, Black version with painted eyes and hair	1949	Effanbee	$495 – $595
Scootles	12-13in (31-33cm)	All-composition	appropriate clothes; all in very good condition	1925	Cameo Doll Co.	$450 – $500
Scootles	13-14in (33-36cm)	All-composition	black version	1949	Cameo Doll Co.	$550 – $650
Scootles	15.5in (39cm)	All-composition	jointed arms, legs and head; painted eyes or sleep eyes; painted hair	1929+	Cameo Doll Co.	$595 – $650
Scootles	15-16in (38-41cm)	All-composition	appropriate clothes; all in very good condition	1925	Cameo Doll Co.	$700 – $750
Scootles	16in (41cm)	All-composition	fully-jointed	1949		$500 – $550
Scootles	20in (51cm)	All-composition	appropriate clothes; all in very good condition	1925	Cameo Doll Co.	$1000 – $1250
Scootles	20in (51cm)	All-composition	sleep eyes		Cameo Doll Co.	$1200 – $1500
Scootles	21in (53cm)	All-composition	boy - fully-jointed, largest size composition, brown sleep side glancing eyes	1940s		$1500+

Name	Size	Material Made	Specific Type of Collectible	Year Made	Manufacturer	Current Price
Scootles	21in (53cm)	All-composition	girl - fully-jointed, largest size composition, green sleep side glancing eyes	1940s		$1500+
Scootles	21in (53cm)	All-composition	jointed arms, legs and head; painted eyes or sleep eyes; painted hair	1929+	Cameo Doll Co.	$1200 – $1500
Scootles		All-composition	fully-jointed with painted eyes and painted and molded hair	1930s		$500 – $600
Scootles		All-composition	rare original combination of a different Scootles head and Kewpie body, sample from Joseph Kallus		Joseph Kallus	***
Scootles		All-composition	rare combination of a different Scootles face on a Kewpie body		Joseph Kallus	***
Scootles	9in (23cm)	All-vinyl	fully-jointed with painted eyes and hair	1960s		$250 – $300
Scootles	10in (25cm)	All-vinyl		1964+	Cameo Doll Co., Jesco, Inc.	$200 – $250
Scootles	12in (31cm)	All-vinyl		1964+	Cameo Doll Co., Jesco, Inc.	$250 – $350
Scootles	14in (36cm)	All-vinyl		1964+	Cameo Doll Co., Jesco, Inc.	$350 – $400
Scootles	16in (41cm)	All-vinyl	sleep eyes and molded hair	1960s-1970s		$450 – $500
Scootles		All-vinyl	painted eyes and rooted hair		Joseph Kallus	$650 – $750
Scootles	10in (25cm)	Cloth		1930s		$400 – $450
Scootles	18.5in (47cm)	Cloth		1930s		$700 – $750
Shaker	2in (5cm)	Glazed Bisque	salt and pepper shakers		J.D. Kestner	$275 – $300
Shakers	2.5in (6cm)	China	made in Germany			$275 – $375
Shakers		Glazed Bisque	talcum powder shakers			$175 – $225
Sissie			doll	1928	Joseph Kallus	
Stick Pin		All-bisque	stick pin			
Stick Pin	1in (3cm)	All-celluloid	no moving parts			$20 – $25
Sugar and Cream set		Jasperware	blue and white			$350+
Superman			made like Howdy Doody	late 1940s	Joseph Kallus	$500 – $600
Tea Set		Glazed Bisque	child's china tea set of Kewpie design, includes teapot, sugar and creamer, plates, saucers, cups			$750 – $1000
Toothpick Holder		Glass			Geo Borgfeldt & Co.	$50 – $75
Tray		Glazed Bisque	some have matching coasters			$1250 set
Vanitie				1921	Joseph Kallus	
Vases		Jasperware	blue and white			$250 – $350

Prices for Jasperware is for blue and white

*** Denotes not enough price samples to compute a reliable range.

Index

About the Author

John Axe is a widely recognized and respected authority in the doll and toy collecting hobby. He is the author of many well received books in this field, including *The Encyclopedia of Celebrity Dolls,* which is now considered a classic research volume, and *The Magic of Merrythought,* his last book that deals exclusively with the products of a single toy company. His hundreds of articles about collecting have appeared in several publications, including the *Doll Reader®* and the *Teddy Bear and friends®* magazines. Like most authorities, he has spent years accumulating facts and documentation and has traveled all over the United States, Canada and Europe to research and photograph the material that he includes in his books and articles.

John Axe has been an active member of the United Federation of Doll Clubs, Inc. for many years and has been appointed to several positions in the national organization, including Chairman of the Modern Competitive Exhibit and Editor of the Souvenir Journal. He has just finished his term as president of the Pittsburgh Doll Club.

He is also and artist who has won prizes in competitive exhibits for his paper dolls of vintage characters and costumes. One of these paper dolls, *Aaron, a Soldier of the American Revolution,* was the souvenir paper doll of the 1987 UFDC Convention.

John Axe holds a degree in Spanish Studies from the University of Valladolid in Spain, and an AB and a MA from Youngstown State University. He has taught Spanish for YWCA classes, in high school and for Penn State University. He presently teaches History at Youngstown State University in Ohio.

Other Books by John Axe
Collectible Boy Dolls
Collectible Dolls in National Costume
The Collectible Dionne Quintuplets
Collectible Black Dolls
Collectible Patsy Dolls and Patsy-Types
Collectible Sonja Henie
Tammy and Dolls You Love to Dress
The Encyclopedia of Celebrity Dolls
Effanbee: A Collector's Encyclopedia 1949-1983
Celebrity Doll Price Guide and Annual
   (with A. Glenn Mandeville)
The Magic of Merrythought
Collecting Modern Dolls
Country Music Singers Paper Dolls
Effanbee's Wee Patsy Paper Dolls & Playhouse
Effanbee's Wee Patsy Paper Dolls & Playhouse "Wee" Edition
Effanbee's Candy Kid & Honey Paper Dolls
Effanbee's Patsyette Paper Doll Family
Figure Skating Champions Paper Dolls
Royal Children Paper Dolls
Tammy and Her Family of Dolls
The Secret of Collecting Girls' Series Books

Connie Harrell was born and raised in the Kansas City, Missouri area not far from Bonniebrook home of Rose O'Neill. She fell in love with Kewpies when one smiled at her from a dusty shelf in a dark antique shop. She has now collected Rose O'Neill original artwork and Kewpie items for 34 years. She has belonged to the *International Rose O'Neill Club* for over 25 years and served as international president in 1982-84 and is chair person for the competitive exhibit at the annual IROC Kewpiesta.

Her interest in doll collecting inspired her to found the *Johnson County Doll and Toy Society* an UFDC (United Federation of Doll Collectors) Club. She served as founding president and regional chairperson.

She presently owns and manages The Doll Cradle, a retail doll and bear store and doll hospital. This will be her 31st year selling, repairing, and appraising dolls in the KC area.